Advanced
Modular
Mathematics

STATISTICS 2

Gerald Westover
Graham Smithers

SECOND
EDITION

COLLINS

nec
NATIONAL
EXTENSION
COLLEGE

Unit S2

Published by HarperCollins Publishers Limited
77–85 Fulham Palace Road
Hammersmith
London W6 8JB

www.CollinsEducation.com
On-line Support for Schools and Colleges

© National Extension College Trust Ltd 2000
First published 2000
ISBN 000 322522 4

This book was written by Gerald Westover and Graham Smithers for the National Extension College Trust Ltd. Part of the material was originally written by Mik Wisnieski and Clifford Taylor.

British Library Cataloguing in Publication Data
A catalogue record for this publication is available from the British Library.

Original internal design: Derek Lee
Cover design and implementation: Terry Bambrook
Project editors: Hugh Hillyard-Parker and Margaret Levin
Page layout: Mary Bishop
Printed and bound: Martins the Printers Ltd., Berwick-upon-Tweed

The authors and publishers thank Dave Wilkins for his comments on this book.

The National Extension College is an educational trust and a registered charity with a distinguished body of trustees. It is an independent, self-financing organisation.

Since it was established in 1963, NEC has pioneered the development of flexible learning for adults. NEC is actively developing innovative materials and systems for distance-learning options from basic skills and general education to degree and professional training.

For further details of NEC resources that support Advanced Modular Mathematics, and other NEC courses, contact NEC Customer Services:

National Extension College Trust Ltd
18 Brooklands Avenue
Cambridge CB2 2HN
Telephone 01223 316644, Fax 01223 313586
Email resources@nec.ac.uk, Home page www.nec.ac.uk

You might also like to visit:

www.fireandwater.com
The book lover's website

UNIT

S2

Contents

S2

Advanced Modular Mathematics

FOREWORD This book is one of a series covering the Edexcel Advanced Subsidiary (AS) and Advanced GCE in Mathematics. It covers all the subject material for Statistics 2 (Unit S2), examined from 2002 onwards.

While this series of text books has been structured to match the Edexcel specification, we hope that the informal style of the text and approach to important concepts will encourage other readers whose final exams are from other Boards to use the books for extra reading and practice. In particular, we have included references to the OCR syllabus (see below).

This book is meant to be *used*: read the text, study the worked examples and work through the Practice questions and Summary exercises, which will give you practice in the basic skills you need for maths at this level. Many exercises, and worked examples, are based on applications of the mathematics in this book. There are many books for advanced mathematics, which include many more exercises: use this book to direct your studies, making use of as many other resources as you can.

There are many features in this book that you will find particularly useful:

- Each **section** covers one discrete area of the new Edexcel specification. The order of topics is exactly the same as in the specification.

- **Practice questions** are given at regular intervals throughout each section. The questions are graded to help you build up your mathematical skills gradually through the section. The **Answers** to these questions come at the end of the relevant section.

- **Summary exercises** are given at the end of each section; these include more full-blown, exam-type questions. Full, worked solutions are given in a separate **Solutions** section at the end of the book.

- In addition, we have provided a complete **Practice examination paper**, which you can use as a 'dummy run' of the actual exam when you reach the end of your studies on S2.

- Alongside most of the headings in this book you will see boxed references, e.g. OCR **S2** 5.12.1 (a) These are for students following the OCR specification and indicate which part of that specification the topic covers.

- Your work on this book will provide opportunities for gathering evidence towards Key Skills, especially in Communication and Application of Number. These opportunities are indicated by a 'key' icon,

  for example: **C** 3.2 (see Appendix 4, p. 72, for more information).

The National Extension College has more experience of flexible-learning materials than any other body (see p. ii). This series is a distillation of that experience: Advanced Modular Mathematics helps to put you in control of your own learning.

Permissions

We are grateful to the Assessment and Qualifications Alliance for permission to reproduce question 3 in the Summary exercise on p. 56, which is taken from one of its past examination papers.

The Assessment and Qualifications Alliance accepts no responsibility whatsoever for the accuracy or method of working in the answer given in the Solutions section, which is entirely the responsibility of the author.

The binomial and Poisson distributions

INTRODUCTION There are two very important discrete distributions – the binomial distribution and the Poisson distribution.

For a binomial distribution we need a yes/no situation with a constant probability of success. For example, if a coin is thrown 50 times and the number of heads is counted, that should give a binomial distribution. In the real world we will attempt to model real situations with binomial distributions.

A Poisson distribution is the distribution of rare events that occur randomly. For example, the number of Prussian soldiers kicked to death by horses in the Franco-German war of 1871 would appear to fit the bill. Indeed, that is where Poisson came up with the idea in the first place! More usual Poisson examples might involve earthquakes, accidents or computer errors – all occur rarely, but, on occasions there could be lots!

It turns out that a Poisson distribution is easier to handle than a binomial distribution and so it is pleasing to learn that in some cases, which we shall define, it is possible to replace a binomial distribution by an approximate Poisson distribution.

The binomial distribution

OCR S1 5.11.3 (a),(d)

The second of our discrete probability distributions (following the uniform distribution in S1) is one of the most important: the **binomial distribution**. We shall illustrate its important principles with a simple example.

Let us assume there is a small factory producing some particular item. In order to monitor the quality of the output produced in the factory an inspector is employed to regularly check the items. This is done by taking a small sample and seeing how many can be classed as faulty or as not faulty. On average 10% of items checked are found to be faulty.

The inspector chooses four items at random from the production line and wants to calculate the following probabilities:

P (0 items are faulty)

P (1 item is faulty)

P (2 items are faulty)

P (3 items are faulty)

P (4 items are faulty)

i.e. he wants to know the distribution of X – the number of faulty items in a sample of 4.

As we shall see this is typical of a problem where the binomial distribution is appropriate. Before proceeding we shall introduce the appropriate terminology.

A binomial situation can be recognised where:

1   an experiment consists of a number (n) of repetitive actions called **trials**

2   each trial has **two mutually exclusive outcomes** (generally referred to as success and failure)

3   the probability of success for each trial is denoted as p and **remains constant**

4   the trials are **independent**

5   we define the random variable X as the number of successes from the n trials.

Clearly for our example, $n = 4$. Success is defined as choosing a faulty item, so $p = 0.1$.

If X is a discrete random variable having a binomial distribution with number of independent trials = n and probability of success at each trial = p, then we write:

$$X \sim B(n, p)$$

where the symbol $\sim$ is read as 'has the distribution'.

and B stands for 'binomial'.

n and p are called the **parameters of the distribution.**

In our example, X is the number of faulty items in a sample of 4 where each item has a probability of $p = 0.1$ of being faulty

so $X \sim B(4, 0.1)$

We now proceed to work out the probability distribution for this random variable.

P(X = 0)

$X = 0$ means that no items are faulty and since each item is not faulty with probability 0.9 independently of the other

$$P(X = 0) \quad = (0.9) \times (0.9) \times (0.9) \times (0.9) = (0.9)^4.$$

P(X = 1)

$X = 1$ means one faulty item and therefore three non-faulty items.

The ways in which this can occur are

$$F\bar{F}\bar{F}\bar{F} \text{ or } \bar{F}F\bar{F}\bar{F} \text{ or } \bar{F}\bar{F}F\bar{F} \text{ or } \bar{F}\bar{F}\bar{F}F$$

where F indicates faulty and $\bar{F}$ indicates not faulty

Hence $P(X = 1) = 4 \times (0.9)^3 \times (0.1)$

P(X = 2)

$X = 2$ means 2 faulty and 2 non-faulty, and proceeding as before we get:

$$\bar{F}\bar{F}FF \text{ or } \bar{F}F\bar{F}F \text{ or } \bar{F}FF\bar{F} \text{ or } F\bar{F}\bar{F}F \text{ or } F\bar{F}F\bar{F} \text{ or } FF\bar{F}\bar{F}$$

giving $P(X = 2) = 6 \times (0.9)^2 \times (0.1)^2$

By now a pattern is emerging and the distribution is:

x	0	1	2	3	4
P($X = x$)	$(0.9)^4$	$4(0.9)^3(0.1)$	$6(0.9)^2(0.1)^2$	$4(0.9)(0.1)^3$	$(0.1)^4$

The remaining probabilities have been calculated using the pattern established by the first three calculations.

This example is representative of all binomial probability distributions and the pattern that is observed in the above table is always present.

The numbers which appear as 'coefficients' are precisely the numbers $\binom{n}{r}$ or ^nC_r, the number of combinations of r things out of n things.

In fact for $X \sim B(n, p)$ there is a formula for P($X = r$) namely

$$P(X = r) = \binom{n}{r} p^r (1 - p)^{n-r}$$

which is made up of the product of

$\binom{n}{r}$ the coefficient representing the number of ways in which r successes can occur in n trials.

p^r representing the r successes occurring with probability p each

$(1 - p)^{n-r}$ representing the $n - r$ failures occurring with probability $1 - p$ each.

Example

$X \sim B(3, 0.4)$ i.e. X is a discrete random variable having a binomial distribution with parameters n (the number of trials) = 3 and
                p (the probability of success at any trial) = 0.4

Write out the probability distribution of X and find E(X) and Var(X)

Solution

Note first that the possible outcomes for B(3, 0.4) are 0, 1, 2, 3

i.e. we can have any number of successes from 0 to 3.

(This is true in general. For B(n, p) the possible outcomes will be 0, 1, 2, ... , n)

Note secondly that since 'success' occurs with probability 0.4, 'failure' occurs with probability 0.6, since success and failure are mutually exclusive.

The probability distribution using techniques employed previously will give us:

x	0	1	2	3
P($X = x$)	$(0.6)^3$	$3(0.6)^2(0.4)$	$3(0.6)(0.4)^2$	$(0.4)^3$

where for example the coefficient for $x = 1$ is obtained by $\binom{3}{1}$ for the number of ways of obtaining one success in three trials.

The probabilities work out to the following as fractions:

x	0	1	2	3
P($X = x$)	$\frac{216}{1000}$	$\frac{432}{1000}$	$\frac{288}{1000}$	$\frac{64}{1000}$

from which it can be readily seen that the probabilities add up to 1.

In this form it is a simple matter to calculate $E(X)$ and $E(X^2)$.

$$E(X) = 0 \times \frac{216}{1000} + 1 \times \frac{432}{1000} + 2 \times \frac{288}{1000} + 3 \times \frac{64}{1000}$$

$$= \frac{1200}{1000} = 1.2$$

$$E(X^2) = 0^2 \times \frac{216}{1000} + 1^2 \times \frac{432}{1000} + 2^2 \times \frac{288}{1000} + 3^2 \times \frac{64}{1000}$$

$$= \frac{2160}{1000} = 2.16$$

$$\Rightarrow \quad Var(X) = E(X^2) - \left(E(X)\right)^2$$

$$= 2.16 - (1.2)^2 = 0.72$$

Now it turns out that

$$E(X) = 3 \times 0.4$$
$$Var(X) = 3 \times 0.4 \times 0.6$$

and this is not a coincidence.

In general for $X \sim B(n, p)$, $E(X) = np$

$$Var(X) = np(1 - p)$$

$$= npq, \text{ where } q \text{ is often used for } 1 - p$$

The proofs of these formulae are not part of the syllabus but you should be familiar with the results.

To summarise:

If $X \sim B(n, p)$ i.e. X has a binomial distribution with number of trials $= n$

and probability of success $= p$, then:

$$P(X = r) = \binom{n}{r} p^r (1 - p)^{n-r}$$

$$E(X) = np$$

$$Var(X) = np(1 - p)$$

Practice questions A

1 Four fair dice are thrown. Find the probability of:

   (a) 3 sixes   (b) 0 sixes.

   (c) What is the expected number of sixes and what is the variance?

2 60% of days are wet. Assuming a binomial model:

   (a) find the probability of four wet days in a week

   (b) what is the expected number of wet days in a week and what is the variance?

3 On average my train is late on 45 journeys out of 100. Next week I shall be making five train journeys. Let X denote the number of times my train will be late.

   (a) State the assumption which must be made for X to be modelled as a binomial distribution.

   C 3.2

   (b) Find the probability my train will be late on all five journeys.

4 Given that $X \sim B(10, 0.4)$, find $P(X = 6)$.

5 Given that $X \sim B(7, 0.6)$, find $P(X = 5)$.

6 30% of dogs have fleas. I've got five dogs. Let X denote the number of my dogs with fleas.

(a) State one assumption that must be made for X to be modelled as a binomial distribution. **C 3.2**

(b) Find the probability that exactly three of my dogs have fleas.

(c) How many of my dogs are expected to have fleas?

(d) Write down the values of $E(X)$ and $Var(X)$.

7 If $X \sim B(10, 0.2)$, find $E(X)$ and $Var(X)$.

8 If $X \sim B(8, p)$ and $E(X) = 2$, find p.

9 If $X \sim B(n, 0.2)$ and $E(X) = 40$, find n.

10 If $X \sim B(n,p)$ and $E(X) = 20$ and $Var(X) = 4$, find the values of n and p.

11 20% of batsmen are bowled first ball. A team has 11 batsmen and X is the number bowled first ball.

(a) State one assumption for X to be modelled as a binomial distribution. Is that assumption reasonable? **C 3.2**

(b) Assuming the binomial model, what is the probability that four of the team are bowled first ball?

Example

10% of items checked on a production line are found to be faulty. If we select ten items from the production line, find the probability that:

(a) 3 items are faulty

(b) 4 or more items are faulty

(c) less than 3 items are faulty

(d) 7 or more items are *non-faulty*.

Solution

Let X = number of items out of 10 which are faulty. Then $X \sim B(10, 0.1)$

(a) $P(X = 3) = \binom{10}{3} (0.1)^3 (0.9)^7$

$= \dfrac{10!}{3!7!} (0.1)^3 (0.9)^7$

$= 0.0574$ (from calculator)

(b) $P(X \geq 4)$ requires working out seven probabilities

A simpler approach is to find $P(X \leq 3)$ and subtract from 1, i.e. use the *complementary* event

$P(X \leq 3) = P(X = 0) + P(X = 1) + P(X = 2) + P(X = 3)$

$= (0.9)^{10} + \binom{10}{1} (0.9)^9 (0.1) + \binom{10}{2} (0.9)^8 (0.1)^2 + \binom{10}{3} (0.9)^7 (0.1)^3$

$= 0.3487 + 0.3874 + 0.1937 + 0.0574$

$= 0.987$ (3 d.p.)

$\Rightarrow \quad P(X \geq 4) = 1 - 0.987 = 0.013$ (3 d.p.)

(c) $P(X < 3) = P(X = 0) + P(X = 1) + P(X = 2)$

$= (0.9)^{10} + \binom{10}{1} (0.9)^9 (0.1) + \binom{10}{2} (0.9)^8 (0.1)^2$

$= 0.9298$

(d) P (7 or 8 or 9 or 10 are good)

$= P$ (3 or 2 or 1 or 0 are faulty) $= P(X \leq 3) = 0.987$ (as in (b))

| **Example** | The office of a large company has recently bought a consignment of ten of the latest photocopying machines for use around the company. The office manager knows from previous experience that there is a 20% probability that any one machine will develop a fault within the first twelve months. The cost of repairing such a fault will be, on average, £125. |

(a) What is the probability that at least eight of the machines will not break down in the first year?

(b) What is the probability that at least one machine will break down?

(c) How much money should be allocated over the next year to the repair budget for these machines?

| **Solution** | (a) P (8 or 9 or 10 are OK) |

$$= \text{P (2 or 1 or 0 faulty)}$$

$$= \binom{10}{2} (0.2)^2 (0.8)^8 + \binom{10}{1} (0.2) (0.8)^9 + (0.8)^{10}$$

$$= 0.678$$

(b) P (at least one fault)

$$= \text{P (1 or 2 or 3 or ... or 10 faults)}$$

$$= 1 - \text{P (0 faults)}$$

$$= 1 - (0.8)^{10} = 0.893$$

(c) For $n = 10, p = 0.2,$

$$\text{Mean} = np = 10 \times 0.2 = 2$$

$\therefore$ We expect 2 to break down

$\therefore$ We should budget for the sum $2 \times 125 = £250$.

Practice questions B

1 25% of people lose their calculator. Assuming a binomial model find, for a class of 15 pupils, the probability that:

(a) less than 3 lose their calculator

(b) at least one loses their calculator.

2 60% of people are overweight. Assuming a binomial model find, for a group of seven friends, the probability that:

(a) three are overweight

(b) three or more are overweight.

3 1 in 10 people are late for class. Assuming a binomial model find, for a class of 12 people, the probability that:

(a) exactly two are late

(b) fewer than two are late.

4 The probability of having blood group A+ is $\frac{1}{3}$.
Four people are in a room. What is the probability that at least two of them have blood group A+?

Comment on the model chosen. **C** 3.2

5 A rifleman hits a target with probability $\frac{1}{4}$.
What is the probability of at least two hits in three rounds.

Comment on the model chosen. **C** 3.2

6 A population of mice is $\frac{2}{3}$ male and $\frac{1}{4}$ pure white.
Assuming independence, find the probability of:

(a) a pure white female

(b) three pure white females

in a sample of five mice.

7 The probability that a patient arriving at a hospital casualty department will be kept in overnight is $\frac{2}{3}$. Find the probability that, among five patients, more than one will be kept in overnight.

8 In a mating experiment designed to produce brown mice, half of the offspring are expected to be brown. Independently of their colour, the offspring are equally likely to be male or female. In a litter of five offspring, what is the probability of obtaining at least two brown females?

9 Given that $X \sim B(8, 0.7)$, find $P(X > 6)$.

10 Given that $X \sim B(7, 0.6)$, find $P(X \leq 3)$.

The Poisson distribution

OCR S2 5.12.3 (a),(c)

The next of our probability distributions is the Poisson (pronounced 'Pwasonn') distribution. We shall see that it has similarities to the binomial and, indeed, in certain circumstances can be used to approximate the binomial distribution.

To illustrate the principles, let us use a simple example. The editor of this book has been checking the accuracy of the proofs before publication. It has been found that on average there are two minor misprints per page. We wish to determine the probability that on a given page there are:

(a)   no misprints

(b)   four or more misprints.

At first sight it does not appear obvious how we can proceed, based on the information given. There is no apparent way of determining such a probability. Clearly if we knew the number of words per page we could calculate the probability of a page containing a misprint, but this is information we are not given. It is in this type of situation that the Poisson distribution can be applied.

The Poisson distribution is a good model in a wide range of situations, the general theme of which is that of rare events happening in time or space. Further examples are:

X = the number of calls per 5 minute period coming into a telephone switchboard

Y = the number of accidents occurring in a factory per week

Z = the number of flaws per m² in a length of material produced in a factory

In each of these situations the following requirements are met:

(a)   The events are rare, or should be!

(b)   Events occur randomly and one at a time

(c)   Events are independent of each other.

(d)   The mean number of events per interval is proportional to the length of the interval.

So, for example, in the example of the factory, if W is the number of accidents occurring in a fortnight then $E(W) = 2E(Y)$ simply because the time interval is twice as long.

> The probabilities for a Poisson distribution are calculated from the formula:
> $$P(X = r) = \frac{e^{-\mu}\mu^r}{r!} \quad r = 0, 1, 2 \ldots$$

where μ is the mean number of occurrences (per unit time or area).

This is an example of a discrete random variable having an infinite number of possible outcomes.

In the example of the misprints per page at the beginning of this section, the average is 2 per page, so μ is 2 and the probability distribution will have the form:

r	0	1	2	3	4 …
$P(X = r)$	e^{-2}	$2e^{-2}$	$\dfrac{4e^{-2}}{2!}$	$\dfrac{8e^{-2}}{3!}$	$\dfrac{16e^{-2}}{4!}$

using the formula above (note that $0! = 1$) and evaluation of these probabilities gives (to 3 d.p.):

r	0	1	2	3	4 …
$P(X = r)$	0.135	0.271	0.271	0.180	0.090 …

It should be noticed that the probabilities rapidly become very small and in fact for the distribution given by adding the above probabilities $P(X \leq 4) = 0.947$ (3 d.p.). This means that $P(X \geq 5) = 0.053$. In practice of course the number of misprints per page will be a finite number.

The Poisson distribution which models this type of phenomenon can in theory take any whole number value ≥ 0, but, as we have seen above, large outcomes have very small (negligible) probabilities.

This obvious discrepancy between the reality of the situation being modelled and the probability distribution being used for the modelling does not invalidate the model however. The Poisson distribution provides a successful model for a diverse range of data arising from a wide variety of sources.

If X has a Poisson distribution with mean μ, we write $X \sim P(\mu)$. [Note that some Examination Boards write this as $X \sim Po(\mu)$.]

Example

For the problem given at the beginning of this section about the number of misprints per page, find the probability of 4 or more misprints per page.

Solution

$X \sim P(2)$

$$\begin{aligned}
P(X \geq 4) &= P \,(4 \text{ or } 5 \text{ or } 6 \text{ or } \dots \text{ misprints}) \\
&= 1 - P \,(0 \text{ or } 1 \text{ or } 2 \text{ or } 3 \text{ misprints}) \\
&= 1 - \left[\frac{e^{-2}2^0}{0!} + \frac{e^{-2}2^1}{1!} + \frac{e^{-2}2^2}{2!} + \frac{e^{-2}2^3}{3!}\right]
\end{aligned}$$

Now take out a factor of e^{-2} and get:

$$= 1 - e^{-2}\left[1 + \frac{2}{1!} + \frac{2^2}{2!} + \frac{2^3}{3!}\right]$$

Now use your calculator and get:

$$= 1 - e^{-2}\,(6.333) = 1 - 0.8571 = 0.143 \quad (3 \text{ d.p.})$$

Example	I expect to receive three letters a week. Use the Poisson distribution to find the probability of receiving:

(a) one letter this week

(b) at least three letters this week

(c) five letters during the next fortnight.

Solution	If X = the number of letters received each week then $X \sim P(3)$.

(a) $\quad P(X = 1) = \dfrac{e^{-3}3^1}{1!} = 0.149$ (3 d.p.)

(b) $\quad P(X \geq 3)$

$= \quad P(3 \text{ or } 4 \text{ or } 5 \text{ or } \dots \text{ letters})$

$= \quad 1 - P(0 \text{ or } 1 \text{ or } 2 \text{ letters})$

$= \quad 1 - \left[\dfrac{e^{-3}3^0}{0!} + \dfrac{e^{-3}3^1}{1!} + \dfrac{e^{-3}3^2}{2!}\right]$

$= \quad 1 - e^{-3}\left[1 + \dfrac{3}{1!} + \dfrac{3^2}{2!}\right] = 0.577$ (3 d.p.)

(c) If Y = the number of letters received in a fortnight then $Y \sim P(6)$

$\quad P(Y = 5) = \dfrac{e^{-6}6^5}{5!} = 0.161$ (3 d.p.)

Practice questions C

1 The mean number of pets per family is two. Assuming a Poisson distribution, find the probability that a family has:

(a) no pets

(b) three pets

(c) fewer than three pets.

2 We expect three flu deaths a week in Birmingham. Assuming a Poisson distribution, find the probability of:

(a) no deaths this week

(b) two or more deaths this week

(c) at least three deaths next week.

3 On average there are four accidents a year on a stretch of road. Assuming a Poisson distribution, find the probability of:

(a) no accidents this year

(b) fewer than four accidents this year.

4 In Africa we expect a famine every two years. Assuming a Poisson distribution, find the probability of:

(a) no more than two famines this year

(b) no famines in the next two years.

5 We expect a hurricane in the UK once in every 10 years. Assuming a Poisson distribution, find the probability of:

(a) no hurricanes in the next 20 years

(b) fewer than two hurricanes in the next 30 years

(c) four hurricanes in the next 40 years.

6 A hospital expects two emergencies a day. It has three empty beds for emergencies at the start of the day. Assuming a Poisson distribution, find the probability that there are not enough beds for emergencies on that day.

7 If $X \sim P(3.5)$, find:

    (a) $P(X = 0)$ (b) $P(X < 3)$.

8 If $X \sim P(1.8)$, find:

    (a) $P(X = 6)$ (b) $P(X \geq 4)$.

9 If $X \sim P(\mu)$ and $P(X = 0) = 0.22313$, find:

    (a) the value of μ (b) $P(X = 2)$ (c) $P(X = \mu)$.

10 If the number of bacterial colonies on a petri dish follow a Poisson distribution with mean number 2.5 per cm^2, find the probability that:

    (a) in 1 cm^2 there will be no bacterial colonies

    (b) in 1 cm^2 there will be more than four bacterial colonies

    (c) in 2 cm^2 there will be less than four bacterial colonies

    (d) in 4 cm^2 there will be six bacterial colonies.

11 You expect 1.5 falls of snow a year. Assuming a Poisson model, after how many years will the probability of no falls of snow equal 0.0111?

12 The number of night calls to a fire station can be modelled by a Poisson distribution with mean 3.8 per night. Find the probability that on a particular night there will be 3 or more calls to the fire station.

State what needs to be assumed about the calls to the fire station in order to justify a Poisson model.   **C** 3.2

The mean and variance of the Poisson distribution   OCR S2 5.12.3 (b)

There is an interesting result about the Poisson distribution. If $X \sim P(\mu)$, then

$$E(X) = \mu \text{ and } Var(X) = \mu$$

If we have some discrete data and there is some evidence that it comes from a Poisson distribution, then further supporting evidence for this belief will be obtained by checking to see if the sample mean and sample variance have similar values. If they are found to be very different, then these would be good grounds for believing that the data comes from a distribution other than the Poisson.

In summary:

> If X is a discrete random variable having a Poisson distribution
> with mean frequency μ per time or space interval, we write
>
> $$X \sim P(\mu)$$
>
> and probabilities can be calculated from the formula:
>
> $$P(X = r) = \frac{\mu^r e^{-\mu}}{r!} \qquad r = 0, 1, 2, \ldots$$
>
> where $E(X) = \mu$
>
> and $Var(X) = \mu$

Practice questions D

1 If $X \sim P(\mu)$ and $E(X) = 2$, find $P(X = 2)$.

2 If $X \sim P(\mu)$ and $Var(X) = 9$, find:

(a) the value of μ

(b) $P(X \leq 3)$.

3 The random variable X follows a Poisson distribution with standard deviation 2. Find $P(X \leq 3)$.

4 The number of cars owned by 200 random families in Leicester was found to be:

No. of cars	0	1	2	3	4	5
No. of families	60	76	40	18	4	2

(a) Find the mean and variance of this sample.

(b) How do the statistics found in (a) support the theory that the number of cars owned follows a Poisson distribution?

(c) Assuming that the number of cars owned follows a Poisson model with the calculated mean, work out the expected frequencies

(d) Comment on your results in (c). **C** 3.2

5 If $X \sim P(\lambda)$ and $E(X) + 7 Var(X) = 16$, find the value of λ.

6 A firm investigated the number of employees suffering injuries while at work. The results below were obtained for a 52-week period:

No. of employees injured in a week	0	1	2	3	4+
No. of weeks	31	17	3	1	0

Give reasons why one might expect this distribution to approximate to a Poisson distribution.

Evaluate the mean and variance of the data and explain why this gives further evidence in favour of a Poisson distribution. **C** 3.2

7 The random variable X follows a Poisson distribution with standard deviation 2.25.

Find $P(X = 2)$.

Poisson approximation to the binomial

OCR S2 5.12.3 (d)

The Poisson distribution is one with wide application in its own right, but its origin lies in an attempt to obtain binomial probabilities for large n. The result is very useful and should be known.

If $X \sim B(n, p)$ where p is small and n is large

then the binomial probabilities can be well approximated by the Poisson distribution having the same mean.

i.e. $X \sim B(n, p) \Rightarrow X \approx P(np)$

where $\approx$ is taken to mean 'is approximately distributed'.

Generally good approximations are obtained for $n > 50$ and $p < 0.1$.

Example

Return to our binomial example (see p. 1) where we were sampling production to check the probability of a given number of faulty items being found. Assume that we now take samples of 100 items. Then the number of faulty items is $X \sim B(100, 0.1)$

(a) Using the binomial formula calculate the probability of 8 faulty items.

(b) Alternatively consider a Poisson model and state its accuracy.

Solution

(a) $P(8 \text{ faults}) = \binom{100}{8} (0.1)^8 (0.9)^{92} = \dfrac{100!}{8! \, 92!} (0.1)^8 (0.9)^{92}$

Now we have a problem because most calculators cannot cope with 100!

We *could* proceed as follows:

$$P(8 \text{ faults}) = \frac{100 \times 99 \times 98 \times 97 \times 96 \times 95 \times 94 \times 93}{1 \times 2 \times 3 \times 4 \times 5 \times 6 \times 7 \times 8} (0.1)^8 (0.9)^{92}$$

$$= 0.1148 \ (4 \text{ d.p.})$$

(b) However, with n large and p small we can use the Poisson approximation.

For the Poisson distribution we have $\mu = np = 10$

And so:

$$X \approx P(10)$$

$$P(X = 8) = \frac{e^{-10} \, 10^8}{8!} = 0.113$$

And so the Poisson approximation in this case is accurate to 2 places of decimals.

Example

In a certain draw, each ticket has a probability of 0.02 of winning a prize. Kevin has 100 tickets for the draw. Using the Poisson approximation, find the probability that he wins more than 3 prizes.

Solution

If X is the number of prizes he wins then

$$X \sim B(100, 0.02)$$

(The actual distribution is binomial since, for each of his 100 tickets, there is a fixed probability of 0.02 of winning.)

$\Rightarrow \quad X \approx P(2) \quad$ since $n = 100 > 50$ and $p = 0.02 < 0.1$, giving $np = 2$.

$\therefore \quad P(X > 3) = P(X = 4) + P(X = 5) + \ldots$

$\qquad\qquad = 1 - P(X = 0) - P(X = 1) - P(X = 2) - P(X = 3)$

$\qquad\qquad = 1 - \left(e^{-2} + 2e^{-2} + \dfrac{2^2 e^{-2}}{2!} + \dfrac{2^3 e^{-2}}{3!} \right)$

$\qquad\qquad = 1 - e^{-2} \left(1 + 2 + 2 + \dfrac{4}{3} \right)$

$\qquad\qquad = 1 - e^{-2} \left(\dfrac{19}{3} \right) = 0.143$

Practice questions E

1 If $X \sim B(60, 0.05)$, explain why $X \approx P(\mu)$ and state the value of μ.

2 If $X \sim B(50, 0.06)$, comment on the validity of replacing the binomial model by an approximate Poisson model.

3 The probability of a rotten peach is 0.015. I buy a consignment of 200 peaches. Using a suitable model, find the probability of fewer than five peaches being rotten.

4 The probability I get drunk on a particular night is 0.001. During the next 4 years (1460 days), what's the probability I get drunk more than 4 times?

5 The probability that a rose has black spot is 0.025. I have 150 roses in the garden. What's the probability that more than 3, but fewer than 7, have black spot?

6 An aircraft has 116 seats. The airline has found, from long experience, that on average 2.5% of people with tickets for a particular flight do not arrive for that flight. If the airline sells 120 seats for a particular flight, determine, using a suitable approximation which should be justified, the probability that more than 116 people arrive for that flight. Determine also the probability that there are empty seats on the flight.

7 An insurance company finds that 0.005 per cent of the population dies from a certain kind of accident each year. Ten thousand people are insured with the company against this risk. Calculate the probability that the company will receive at least four claims for this accident in any given year.

8 The number of cars passing a house between 8.00 am and 9.00 am on a weekday is a random variable X. Give a condition under which X may be modelled by a Poisson distribution.

Suppose that $X \sim P(3.4)$. Calculate:
(a) $P(X \geq 4)$ (b) $P(X = 0)$

In a random sample of 100 weekdays, the number of days on which no cars pass the house between 8.00 am and 9.00 am is Y.

Explain why Y can be modelled approximately by a Poisson distribution and find $P(Y = 2)$. **C** 3.2

SUMMARY EXERCISE

1 Random variable X is 'the number of bad eggs in a batch of 10 eggs' where for each egg there is a probability of 0.15 of it being bad. State the distribution of X and find $P(X \geq 4)$, $P(X > E(X))$.

2 A school decides to have its fire drill in a particular week. They program a computer to decide when the drill will be held(!). The computer chooses days at random with a probability of $p = 0.35$ of choosing any particular day. No one thought to tell the computer to choose only one day. Let X be the number of fire drills held in that 5-day week.

(a) Calculate the probability distribution of X and state its mean and variance.

(b) What value of p should they choose to give an expected value of one fire drill during the week? What would be the probability of more than one fire drill?

3 A certain person can hit the bullseye on a dartboard with probability 0.4. How many throws must he make to have a probability of at least 0.9 of hitting the bullseye at least once?

4 If $X \sim B(10, 0.2)$, find:
(a) $P(X \leq 3)$ (b) $P(X > 6)$ (c) $P(4 \leq X < 8)$

5 If $X \sim B(10, 0.8)$, find $P(X \leq 3)$.

6 A shop sells a particular make of radio at a rate of 4 per week on average. The number sold in a week is thought to have a Poisson distribution.

(a) Using a Poisson distribution, find the probability that the shop sells at least 2 in a week.

(b) Find the smallest number that can be in stock at the beginning of a week in order to have at least a 99% probability of being able to meet all demands during that week.

(c) Comment on the applicability of a Poisson distribution. **C** 3.2

7 The number of accidents per week at a certain intersection has a Poisson distribution with parameter 2.5. Find the probability that

(a) exactly 5 accidents will occur in a week,

(b) more than 5 accidents will occur in 2 weeks.

8 $X \sim B(35, 0.1)$.

Use the Poisson approximation to the binomial distribution to find $P(X \leq 5)$.

SUMMARY

In this section we have seen that **a binomial distribution**

- is a discrete distribution
- represents a yes/no situation with a constant probability of success
- can be symbolised by $X \sim B(n, p)$, where the random variable X is the result of n trials, with p the probability of success for each trial.

The relevant formulae are:

- $P(X = r) = \binom{n}{r} p^r (1 - p)^{n-r}$ $\left(\text{when } \binom{n}{r} = {}^nC_r = \dfrac{n!}{(n-r)! \, r!} \right)$

- $E(X) = np$
- $\text{Var}(X) = npq$ (where $q = 1 - p$)

We have also seen that a **Poisson distribution**:

- is a discrete distribution
- is a distribution of rare events that occur randomly
- can be symbolised by $X \sim P(\mu)$, where the random variable X has mean μ.

The relevant formulae are:

- $P(X = r) = \dfrac{e^{-\mu}\mu^r}{r!}$

- $E(X) = \mu$
- $\text{Var}(X) = \mu$ $\left(\text{so } E(X) = \text{Var}(X) \right)$

Finally, we saw that a **binomial distribution can be replaced by an approximate Poisson distribution** if:

$\quad n > 50$ and $p < 0.1$

In that case $X \sim B(n,p) \Rightarrow X \approx P(np)$.

ANSWERS

Practice questions A

1 (a) 0.0154   (b) 0.482   (c) $\dfrac{2}{3}, \dfrac{5}{9}$

2 (a) 0.2903   (b) 4.2, 1.68

3 (a) Each day, the probability of a train being late is 0.45

   (b) 0.0185

4 0.111

5 0.261

6 (a) Each dog has a 30% probability of fleas. This is unrealistic – if one gets fleas, they'll all have fleas!

   (b) 0.1323   (c) 1.5   (d) 1.5, 1.05

7 2, 1.6

8 0.25

9 200

10 $n = 25$, $p = 0.8$

   [Hint: $np = 20$, $npq = 4$ $\therefore 20q = 4$ etc.]

11 (a) Each batsman has a 20% probability of being bowled first ball. This is unrealistic: 'tail enders' (i.e. the weakest batsmen) are much more likely to be bowled first ball than specialist batsmen.

   (b) 0.1107

Practice questions B

1 (a) 0.236   (b) 0.9866

2 (a) 0.1935   (b) 0.9037

3 (a) 0.2301   (b) 0.659

4 0.407. This might be invalid if they are all members of the same family

5 0.156. Unrealistic – the rifleman should get better with each round.

6 (a) $\frac{1}{12}$ (b) 4.86×10^{-3}

7 0.95473

8 0.36719

9 0.255

10 0.28979

Practice questions C

1 (a) 0.1353   (b) 0.18   (c) 0.68

2 (a) 0.05   (b) 0.80   (c) 0.58

3 (a) 0.018   (b) 0.4335

4 (a) 0.99   (b) 0.37

   [Hint: for (a) Mean = 0.5.]

5 (a) 0.14 ($\mu = 2$) (b) 0.20 ($\mu = 3$)

   (c) 0.20 ($\mu = 4$)

6 0.143

7 (a) 0.0302   (b) 0.32

8 (a) 0.00781   (b) 0.109

9 (a) 1.5   (b) 0.251

   (c) 0 (μ is not an integer)

10 (a) 0.0821   (b) 0.109

   (c) 0.265 ($\mu = 5$)   (d) 0.0631 ($\mu = 10$)

11 3

12 0.731

   Calls must be rare events and occur at random.

Practice questions D

1 0.271

2 (a) 9   (b) 0.0212

3 0.433 (mean = variance = 4)

4 (a) 1.18, 1.1676

   (b) Mean ≈ variance for this sample ∴ assume mean = variance for population as a whole

   (c) 61, 73, 43, 17, 5, 1 (to the nearest integer)

   (d) The model fits the sample fairly well.

5 2

6 Injuries are rare events and (should!) occur at random. Sample mean = 0.5 and sample variance = 0.481

   ∴ mean ≈ variance for this sample

   ∴ in the population as a whole it is likely that mean = variance

   ∴ a Poisson distribution is likely.

7 0.08111 (mean = 5.0625)

Practice questions E

1 $n = 60 > 50$, $p = 0.05 < 0.1$

   ∴ approximately Poisson

   Mean = $np = 3$ ∴ $\mu = 3$

2 $n = 50$ (rather than > 50)

   but $p = 0.06 < 0.1$ as required

   On balance we can still assume an approximate Poisson model, but it's a borderline decision.

3 0.815

4 0.0168

5 0.4299

6 Originally $X \sim B(120, 0.025)$.

   Since $n > 50$, $p < 0.1 \Rightarrow X \approx P(3)$.

   $P(X \leq 3) = 0.647$, $P(X \geq 5) = 0.185$

7 0.0018

8 The passing of a car needs to be a rare event and it must happen randomly.

   (a) 0.442   (b) 0.03337

   Y is approximately Poisson because $n = 100 > 50$ and $p = 0.03337 < 0.1$

   ∴ $Y \sim P(3.337)$ ∴ 0.1979

SECTION

2

Continuous random variables

INTRODUCTION

In S1 we looked at discrete random variables and investigated probability, mode, median, quartiles, mean and variance. We are now going to do the same for continuous random variables.

For this section you will need to be able to:

- differentiate powers of x and work out turning values
- integrate powers of x and work out areas.

If you feel unsure, then you should refer to the relevant sections in P1.

Continuous random variables

OCR S3 5.13.1 (a)

Discrete random variables are used to model situations in which discrete data is obtained. These quite often refer to situations which start with the phrase 'X is the number of …'; in other words, they refer to situations in which counting is taking place.

Continuous random variables are used to model data sets which are continuous in nature and are usually the result of making a measurement, e.g. heights of people or the time taken to complete a journey.

Continuous data is usually grouped into intervals and is represented graphically by a histogram where the areas of columns correspond to the frequencies within each interval. The mid-points of these columns can be joined by a continuous curve, thereby bringing out the continuous nature of the data even more. Correspondingly the important features of continuous random variables are:

(a) that they can be represented graphically by continuous curves

(b) that areas under the curve correspond to probabilities.

Because continuous random variables correspond to continuous curves, they are defined in terms of continuous functions called **probability density functions**.

A probability density function (PDF) defined over the interval $a \leq x \leq b$

is a function f(x) with the properties

(a) $\displaystyle\int_a^b f(x)\, dx = 1$ (b) f(x) ≥ 0 for all $a \leq x \leq b$

This amounts to saying that all the probabilities sum to 1 and all probabilities are positive or zero and correspond to similar results for discrete random variables.

It may be that a or b (or both) are infinite and indeed this is the case with the most important continuous distribution (the normal distribution – described in unit S1).

Finding probabilities for continuous random variables amounts to doing integrations as illustrated in the first example.

Example

The continuous variable X has a PDF given by:

$$f(x) = \begin{cases} \frac{1}{5}(4x + 3) & \text{for } 0 \leq x \leq 1 \\ 0 & \text{elsewhere} \end{cases}$$

(a)   Verify that $f(x)$ is a PDF.

(b)   Find $P(0 \leq X \leq 0.75)$.

Solution

(a)   We must show that $\int_0^1 f(x)\,dx = 1$

as this is required by the definition of a PDF.

We have $\int_0^1 \frac{1}{5}(4x + 3)\,dx \quad = \frac{1}{5}\left[2x^2 + 3x\right]_0^1$

$$= \frac{1}{5}(5 - 0) \ = 1$$

So $f(x)$ behaves like a PDF and we conclude that X is a continuous random variable.

(b) $P(0 \leq X \leq 0.75) \quad = \int_0^{0.75} \frac{1}{5}(4x + 3)\ dx$

$$= \frac{1}{5}\left[2x^2 + 3x\right]_0^{0.75} = 0.675$$

Therefore the probability that X takes a value between 0 and 0.75 is 0.675.

Example

A continuous distribution is defined by the PDF:

$$f(x) = \begin{cases} c\left(\frac{6}{5}x^2 + 10\right) & \text{for } 0 \leq x \leq 5 \text{ where } c \text{ is a constant} \\ 0 & \text{elsewhere} \end{cases}$$

(a)   Find c.

(b)   Determine the probabilities for the intervals 0 to 1, 1 to 2, 2 to 3, 3 to 4 and 4 to 5.

Solution

(a) $\displaystyle\int_0^5 f(x)\,dx\ = 1$ (The basic requirement for a PDF)

$$\Rightarrow \int_0^5 c\left(\tfrac{6}{5}x^2 + 10\right)dx\ = 1)$$

$$\Rightarrow c\left[\tfrac{2}{5}x^3 + 10x\right]_0^5 = 1$$

$$\Rightarrow c\left[0.4(5^3) + 50\right] = 1 \quad \text{giving } c = \tfrac{1}{100}$$

(b) We now need to evaluate $\displaystyle\int_a^b f(x)\,dx$ for the given intervals:

The first gives $\dfrac{1}{100}\left[\tfrac{2}{5}x^3 + 10x\right]_0^1$ using the known value for c, and which on evaluation gives 0.104. That is, the probability that X takes a value in the interval 0 to 1 is 0.104.

Similarly for the other intervals we have:

$$\dfrac{1}{100}\left[\tfrac{2}{5}x^3 + 10x\right]_1^2 \quad\quad \text{giving } 0.232 - 0.104\ = 0.128$$

$$\dfrac{1}{100}\left[\tfrac{2}{5}x^3 + 10x\right]_2^3 \quad\quad \text{giving } 0.408 - 0.232\ = 0.176$$

$$\dfrac{1}{100}\left[\tfrac{2}{5}x^3 + 10x\right]_3^4 \quad\quad \text{giving } 0.656 - 0.408\ = 0.248$$

$$\dfrac{1}{100}\left[\tfrac{2}{5}x^3 + 10x\right]_4^5 \quad\quad \text{giving } 1.000 - 0.656\ = 0.344$$

Double-checking shows us that if we sum these probabilities they total to 1.000. We shall return to examine specific probability distributions and their properties in more detail in the next section(s).

An important property of continuous random variables which follows from the property

$$\int_a^a f(x)\,dx\ = 0$$

is that

    $P(X = a) = 0$ for all a.

A consequence of this property is that, for example:

    $P(X \le a) = P(X < a)$

This property only holds for continuous random variables, however.

Practice questions A

1   A continuous variable X has a PDF given by

$$f(x) = \begin{cases} Kx & \text{for } 0 \leq x \leq 2 \\ 0 & \text{otherwise} \end{cases}$$

Illustrate with a sketch. Find:

(a) K (b) $P(X \leq 1.2)$

2   The continuous variable X has a PDF given by

$$f(x) = \begin{cases} Kx^2 & \text{for } 0 \leq x \leq 2 \\ 0 & \text{otherwise} \end{cases}$$

Illustrate with a sketch. Find:

(a) K (b) $P(X \leq 0.6)$.

3   The continuous variable X has a PDF given by

$$f(x) = \begin{cases} K + x & \text{for } 0 \leq x \leq 1 \\ 0 & \text{otherwise} \end{cases}$$

Illustrate with a sketch. Find:

(a) K (b) $P(X \geq 0.2)$

4   The continuous variable X has a PDF given by

$$f(x) = \begin{cases} K(2 - x) & \text{for } 0 \leq x \leq 2 \\ 0 & \text{otherwise} \end{cases}$$

Illustrate with a sketch. Find:

(a) K (b) $P(X \leq 0.8)$

5   The continuous variable X has a PDF given by

$$f(x) = \begin{cases} Kx(1 - x) & \text{for } 0 \leq x \leq 1 \\ 0 & \text{otherwise} \end{cases}$$

Illustrate with a sketch. Find:

(a) K (b) $P(X \leq 0.6)$

6   The continuous variable X has a PDF given by

$$f(x) = \begin{cases} Kx & \text{for } 0 \leq x \leq 1 \\ K(2 - x) & \text{for } 1 \leq x \leq 2 \\ 0 & \text{otherwise} \end{cases}$$

Illustrate with a sketch. Find:

(a) K (b) $P(X \geq 0.5)$

7   A variable X has a PDF given by

$$f(x) = \begin{cases} \dfrac{4}{3x^2} & \text{for } 1 \leq x \leq a \\ 0 & \text{otherwise} \end{cases}$$

(a) Find the value of a.

(b) Find y so that $P(1 \leq X \leq y) = \frac{1}{4}$

8   Petrol is delivered to a garage every Friday evening. At this garage the weekly demand for petrol, in thousands of units, is a continuous random variable X distributed with a PDF of the form

$$f(x) = \begin{cases} 2.4x\,(b - x) & \text{for } 0 \leq x \leq 1 \\ 0 & \text{otherwise} \end{cases}$$

(a) Find the value of b

(b) If the storage tanks at this garage are filled to their total capacity of 900 units every Friday evening, what is the probability that in any given week the garage will be unable to meet the demand for petrol?

9   A radio valve has a life of X hours. If X is distributed according to the density function $\dfrac{200}{x^2}$ $(x \geq 200)$,

find the probability that neither of 2 such valves will have to be replaced during the first 300 hours of operation.

The cumulative distribution function

OCR S3 5.13.1 (c)

If X is a continuous random variable with PDF

$$\begin{cases} f(x) & a \leq x \leq b \\ 0 & \text{elsewhere} \end{cases}$$

then we can define a new function $F(x)$ called the **cumulative distribution function** (CDF) by the following:

$$F(x) = \int_a^x f(t)\,dt = P(X \le x)$$

The usefulness of this function is best illustrated by an example.

Example

Random variable X has PDF given by:

$$f(x) = \begin{cases} \dfrac{3}{4}x\,(2-x) & 0 \le x \le 2 \\ 0 & \text{otherwise} \end{cases}$$

Find $F(x)$, the CDF of this random variable.

Find also $F(0)$, $F(1)$ and $F(2)$ and give a interpretation of these values.

Solution

According to the definition:

$$F(x) = P(X \le x) = \int_0^x \frac{3}{4}t\,(2-t)\,dt$$

(Note: t is a dummy variable in this integration, which is introduced to avoid confusion with the x that appears as the upper limit of the integral.)

$$\Rightarrow \quad F(x) = \frac{3}{4}\int_0^x (2t - t^2)\,dt$$

$$\Rightarrow \quad F(x) = \frac{3}{4}\left[\frac{2t^2}{2} - \frac{t^3}{3}\right]_0^x$$

$$\Rightarrow \quad F(x) = \frac{3}{4}\left[\left(x^2 - \frac{x^3}{3}\right) - (0)\right]$$

$$\Rightarrow \quad F(x) = \frac{3x^2}{4} - \frac{x^3}{4}$$

$$\therefore \quad F(0) = 0$$

$$F(1) = \frac{3}{4} - \frac{1}{4} = \frac{1}{2}$$

$$F(2) = \frac{3}{4}(4) - \frac{8}{4} = 1$$

The interpretations are:

$$P(X \le 0) = 0$$

$$P(X \le 1) = \frac{1}{2}$$

$$P(X \le 2) = 1$$

and these results make sense when we consider the graph of the PDF (see Fig. 2.1).

Figure 2.1

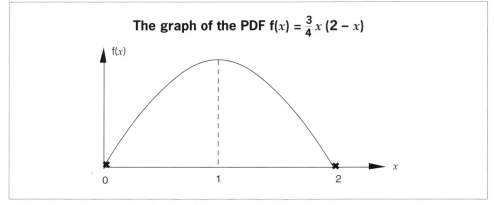

The graph of the PDF $f(x) = \frac{3}{4}x(2-x)$

There is no probability below the value $x = 0$.

By symmetry exactly half the probability is to the left of $x = 1$.

All of the probability is taken up by the value $x = 2$.

It turns out to be useful if the CDF takes a value for every x that is input and the complete definition of $F(x)$ in this example is:

$$F(x) = \begin{cases} 0 & x < 0 \\ \dfrac{3x^2}{4} - \dfrac{x^3}{4} & 0 \le x \le 2 \\ 1 & x \ge 2 \end{cases}$$

The graph of $F(x)$ is shown in Fig. 2.2.

Figure 2.2

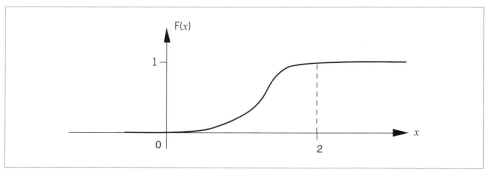

We have seen that the CDF is obtained from the PDF by integrating

i.e. $$F(x) = \int_a^x f(t)\, dt$$

and the value $F(x_0)$ for example gives the accumulated probability up to the value $x = x_0$, i.e. $F(x_0) = P(X \le x_0)$.

Because of the relationship between differentiating and integrating we can obtain the PDF from the CDF by differentiating

i.e. $$f(x) = \frac{d}{dx}(F(x))$$

You should check that this works with the example just completed.

Practice questions B

1 Find the CDF for the distributions in questions 1 to 5 in Practice questions A.

2 Refer back to question 6 in Practice questions A.

If F(x) is the corresponding CDF find F(0.5), F(1) and F(1.5).

3 A random variable X has a CDF F(x) given by:

$$F(x) = \begin{cases} 0 & x < 1 \\ \frac{x}{8}(1 + x^2) & 1 \le x \le 2 \\ 1 & x > 2 \end{cases}$$

Find: (a) the PDF f(x) of the random variable X

(b) P($1.2 \le X \le 1.4$)

4 A continuous PDF is given by:

$$f(x) = \begin{cases} Kx^3 & \text{for } 0 \le x \le 1 \\ 0 & \text{otherwise} \end{cases}$$

Find: (a) the value of K

(b) the CDF.

5 A continuous PDF is given by:

$$f(x) = \begin{cases} 1 + Kx & \text{for } 0 \le x \le 2 \\ 0 & \text{otherwise} \end{cases}$$

Find: (a) the value of K

(b) the CDF.

6 A random variable X has a CDF F(x) given by:

$$F(x) = \begin{cases} 0 & x < 1 \\ \sqrt{x} - 1 & 1 \le x \le 4 \\ 1 & x > 4 \end{cases}$$

Find: (a) the PDF f(x) of the random variable X

(b) P($X \le 2$).

7 A random variable X has a CDF F(x) given by:

$$F(x) = \begin{cases} 0 & x < 0.2 \\ \frac{5}{3} - \frac{1}{3x} & 0.2 \le x \le 0.5 \\ 1 & x > 0.5 \end{cases}$$

Find: (a) the PDF f(x) of the random variable X

(b) P($X \le 0.3$).

Mode and median for a continuous random variable   OCR S3 5.13.1 (c)

We have met the ideas of mode and median of data in unit S1.

We define the mode of a continuous random variable X as the value of X where the PDF of X takes the greatest value.

The median of X is the 'middle' value. Therefore P($X \le$ median) $= \frac{1}{2}$.

More precisely, if X is a random variable with PDF

$$\begin{cases} f(x) & a \le x \le b \\ 0 & \text{elsewhere} \end{cases}$$

then, by the usual calculus of turning points, any mode will be a local maximum of the probability curve and so will be found by solving $f'(x) = 0$ (unless $f(x)$ has a greater value, in which case the mode can be written down by inspection). The median m is given by solving

$$\int_a^m f(x) \, dx = \frac{1}{2}$$

or equivalently:

$$F(x) = \frac{1}{2}, \text{ if F}(x) \text{ is known.}$$

Example	A random variable X has PDF given by

$$f(x) = \begin{cases} cx(4-x)^2 & 0 \le x \le 4 \\ 0 & \text{otherwise} \end{cases}$$

(a) Find c.

(b) Give a sketch of the PDF of X.

(c) Find the mode of X.

Solution	(a) For $f(x)$ to be a PDF it must satisfy $\displaystyle\int_a^b f(x)\,dx = 1$

$$\Rightarrow \int_0^4 cx(4-x)^2\,dx = 1$$

$$\Rightarrow c\int_0^4 (16x - 8x^2 + x^3)\,dx = 1$$

$$\Rightarrow c\left[8x^2 - \frac{8x^3}{3} + \frac{x^4}{4}\right]_0^4 = 1 \quad \Rightarrow c\left[128 - \frac{512}{3} + 64\right] = 1$$

$$\Rightarrow c = \frac{3}{64}$$

Hence $f(x) = \begin{cases} \dfrac{3}{64}x(4-x)^2 & 0 \le x \le 4 \\ 0 & \text{elsewhere} \end{cases}$ is the PDF of X

(b) It is often helpful to give a sketch of a PDF, even if the question doesn't ask for it.

In this example the sketch is as in Fig. 2.3.

Figure 2.3	

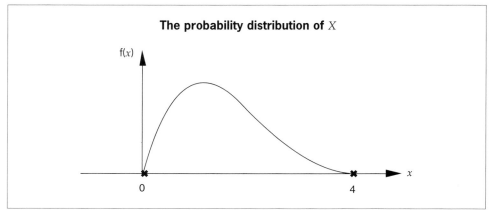

The probability distribution of X

(c) The mode of X is found by solving $f'(x) = 0$

$$f(x) = \frac{3}{64}x(4-x)^2 = \frac{3x}{4} - \frac{3x^2}{8} + \frac{3x^3}{64}$$

$$\Rightarrow f'(x) = \frac{3}{4} - \frac{6x}{8} + \frac{9x^2}{64}$$

$$f'(x) = 0 \Rightarrow \frac{3}{4} - \frac{6x}{8} + \frac{9x^2}{64} = 0$$

$$\Rightarrow \quad 9x^2 - 48x + 48 = 0$$
$$\Rightarrow \quad 3x^2 - 16x + 16 = 0$$
$$\Rightarrow \quad (3x - 4)(x - 4) = 0$$
$$\Rightarrow \quad x = \frac{4}{3}, \ x = 4$$

It is obvious from our sketch that $x = \frac{4}{3}$ is the value required, and $x = \frac{4}{3}$ is the mode of f(X).

Example

The random variable X has PDF

$$f(x) = \begin{cases} \dfrac{1}{72}x & \text{for } 0 \le x \le 12 \\[2mm] 0 & \text{otherwise} \end{cases}$$

Find the median of X.

Solution

M, the median is given by:

$$\int_0^M \frac{1}{72}x \, dx = \frac{1}{2} \quad \Rightarrow \quad \left[\frac{x^2}{144}\right]_0^M = \frac{1}{2}$$
$$\Rightarrow \quad \frac{M^2}{144} = \frac{1}{2}$$
$$\Rightarrow \quad M^2 = 72$$
$$\Rightarrow \quad M = \sqrt{72} \approx 8.49$$

(This result can easily be confirmed by considering the graph of f(x) and using areas of triangles which is left as an exercise for you.)

Example

The random variable X has PDF

$$f(x) = \begin{cases} 16x + 2 & \text{for } 0 \le x \le 0.25 \\[2mm] 0 & \text{otherwise} \end{cases}$$

Illustrate with a sketch and hence write down the mode of X.

Solution

The required sketch is as shown in Fig. 2.4.

Figure 2.4

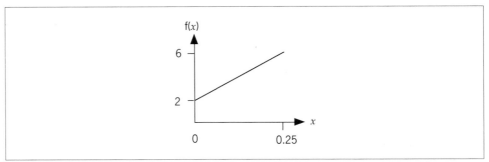

The PDF is at its greatest value when $x = 0.25$.

$\therefore$ the mode of X is 0.25.

[Note: Don't be too anxious to start differentiating when the mode is required. Do a rough sketch first. As in this case, the mode may be the greatest value, and not a maximum.]

Example

The random variable X has PDF

$$f(x) = \begin{cases} 4x + 1 & \text{for } 0 \leq x \leq 0.5 \\ 0 & \text{otherwise} \end{cases}$$

Find:

(a)   the lower quartile

(b)   the upper quartile

(c)   the interquartile range.

Solution

(a)   The lower quartile Q_1 is given by:

$$\int_0^{Q_1} (4x + 1)\, dx = 0.25$$

$$\Rightarrow \quad \left[2x^2 + x \right]_0^{Q_1} = 0.25$$

$$\Rightarrow \quad 2Q_1^2 + Q_1 - 0.25 = 0$$

Solving this quadratic gives us:

$$Q_1 = \frac{-1 \pm \sqrt{3}}{4}$$

$$\therefore \quad Q_1 = \frac{\sqrt{3} - 1}{4} \quad \text{(or 0.183 to 3 d.p.)}$$

(b)   The upper quartile Q_3 is given by:

$$\int_0^{Q_3} (4x + 1)\, dx = 0.75$$

$$\Rightarrow \quad \left[2x^2 + x \right]_0^{Q_3} = 0.75$$

$$\Rightarrow \quad 2Q_3^2 + Q_3 - 0.75 = 0$$

Solving this quadratic gives us:

$$Q_3 = \frac{-1 \pm \sqrt{7}}{4}$$

$$\therefore \quad Q_3 = \frac{\sqrt{7} - 1}{4} \quad \text{(or 0.411 to 3 d.p.)}$$

(c)   The interquartile range is given by $Q_3 - Q_1$.

$$\therefore \quad Q_3 - Q_1 \quad = \left(\frac{\sqrt{7} - 1}{4} - \frac{\sqrt{3} - 1}{4} \right)$$

$$= \frac{\sqrt{7} - \sqrt{3}}{4} \text{ (or 0.228 to 3 d.p.)}$$

Practice questions C

1   For each of the following PDFs:

(i)   illustrate with a sketch

(ii)   find the value of K

(iii)   find the mode.

(a) $f(x) = \begin{cases} Kx & 0 \leq x \leq 2 \\ K(4 - x) & 2 \leq x \leq 4 \\ 0 & \text{otherwise} \end{cases}$

(b) $f(x) = \begin{cases} Kx & \text{for } 0 \leq x \leq 1 \\ 0 & \text{otherwise} \end{cases}$

(c) $f(x) = \begin{cases} Kx(3 - x) & 0 \leq x \leq 3 \\ 0 & \text{otherwise} \end{cases}$

(d) $f(x) = \begin{cases} Kx^2(2 - x) & 0 \leq x \leq 2 \\ 0 & \text{otherwise} \end{cases}$

2   A random variable X has PDF given by

$$f(x) = \begin{cases} Kx & 0 \leq x \leq 3 \\ 0 & \text{otherwise} \end{cases}$$

Illustrate with a sketch. Find:

(a) K (b) median.

3   A random variable X has PDF given by

$$f(x) = \begin{cases} 3x^2 & 0 \leq x \leq 1 \\ 0 & \text{otherwise} \end{cases}$$

Find the median.

4   A random variable X has PDF given by

$$f(x) = \begin{cases} \dfrac{x^3}{4} & 0 \leq x \leq 2 \\ 0 & \text{otherwise} \end{cases}$$

Find:

(a) the median   (b) the lower quartile

(c) the upper quartile   (d) the interquartile range.

State the value of the mode.

5   Find the mode of X where X has the PDF

$$f(x) = \begin{cases} k(9 + 12x - x^3) & 0 \leq x \leq 3 \\ 0 & \text{otherwise} \end{cases}$$

6   The PDF of X is given by

$$f(x) = \begin{cases} \dfrac{x}{24} & 0 \leq x \leq 4 \\ \dfrac{1}{4} - \dfrac{x}{48} & 4 \leq x \leq 12 \\ 0 & \text{otherwise} \end{cases}$$

Sketch the PDF of X and find $P(2 < X < 6)$.
Write down the mode and calculate the median.

7   A random variable X has a PDF given by

$$f(x) = \begin{cases} K & 0 \leq x \leq 1 \\ K(2 - x) & 1 \leq x \leq 2 \\ 0 & \text{otherwise} \end{cases}$$

Illustrate with a sketch.

Find:

(a) K (b) median.

Mean and variance for a continuous random variable   OCR S3 5.13.1 (b)

We met the idea of mean and variance in unit S1. For a *discrete* random variable X, we had:

$$E(X) \quad = \Sigma x_i p_i$$

and $$\text{Var}(X) = \Sigma x_i^2 p_i - [E(X)]^2$$

i.e. $$\text{Var}(X) = E(X^2) - [E(X)]^2$$

For a *continuous random variable* X with PDF given by:

$$\begin{cases} f(x) & a \le x \le b \\ 0 & \text{otherwise} \end{cases}$$

we have $E(X) = \displaystyle\int_a^b x\,f(x)\,dx$

and $\text{Var}(X) = \displaystyle\int_a^b x^2\,f(x)\,dx - \left[E(X)\right]^2$

Example

A random variable X has PDF given by:

$$f(x) = \begin{cases} \dfrac{x}{8} & 0 \le x \le 4 \\ 0 & \text{otherwise} \end{cases}$$

Illustrate with a sketch. Find $E(X)$ and $\text{Var}(X)$

Solution

The PDF is linear and we get:

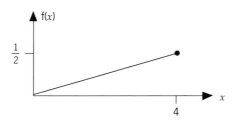

with $f(x) = \dfrac{x}{8}$

$$\therefore \quad E(X) = \int_0^4 x\ f(x)\,dx$$

$$= \int_0^4 x \cdot \frac{x}{8}\,dx = \int_0^4 \frac{x^2}{8}\,dx$$

$$= \left[\frac{x^3}{24}\right]_0^4 = 2\tfrac{2}{3}$$

$$\therefore \quad \text{Var}(X) = \int_0^4 x^2\,f(x)\,dx - \left(2\tfrac{2}{3}\right)^2$$

$$= \int_0^4 x^2 \cdot \frac{x}{8}\,dx - \left(2\tfrac{2}{3}\right)^2$$

$$= \int_0^4 \frac{x^3}{8}\,dx - \left(2\tfrac{2}{3}\right)^2$$

$$= \left[\frac{x^4}{32}\right]_0^4 - \left(2\tfrac{2}{3}\right)^2$$

$$= 8 - 7\tfrac{1}{9} = \frac{8}{9}$$

$$\therefore \quad E(X) = 2\tfrac{2}{3} \text{ and Var}(X) = \frac{8}{9}$$

Practice questions D

1 For each of the following PDF
  (i) illustrate with a sketch
  (ii) find the mean
  (iii) find the variance

  (a) $f(x) = \begin{cases} 3x^2 & 0 \le x \le 1 \\ 0 & \text{otherwise} \end{cases}$

  (b) $f(x) = \begin{cases} 6x(1-x) & 0 \le x \le 1 \\ 0 & \text{otherwise} \end{cases}$

  (c) $f(x) = \begin{cases} 0.5 + x & 0 \le x \le 1 \\ 0 & \text{otherwise} \end{cases}$

  (d) $f(x) = \begin{cases} \dfrac{2x}{3} & 0 \le x \le 1 \\ 1 - \dfrac{x}{3} & 1 \le x \le 3 \end{cases}$

2 The PDF of the variable X is given by

  $f(x) = \begin{cases} K(12 + 4x - x^2) & 0 \le x \le 6 \\ 0 & \text{otherwise} \end{cases}$

  Show that $K = \dfrac{1}{72}$ and hence find $E(X)$.

  Also find $P(X \ge 4)$.

3 The random variable X has PDF given by

  $f(x) = \begin{cases} Kx(6-x)^2 & 0 \le x \le 6 \\ 0 & \text{otherwise} \end{cases}$

  Show that $K = \dfrac{1}{108}$.

  Hence find (a) $E(X)$ (b) $Var(X)$ (c) mode of X.

4 The probability that a baker will have sold all his loaves X hours after baking is given by the PDF

  $f(x) = \begin{cases} K(36 - x) & 0 \le x \le 6 \\ 0 & \text{otherwise} \end{cases}$

  Show that $K = \dfrac{1}{198}$ and sketch the PDF.

  Calculate the mean value and the probability that the baker will have some bread left after five hours.

5 A variable X has a PDF given as follows

  $f(x) = \begin{cases} \dfrac{1}{4} & 0 \le x \le 2 \\ \dfrac{k}{8} & 4 \le x \le 8 \\ 0 & \text{otherwise} \end{cases}$

  Sketch the PDF and hence find the value of K.
  Find:
  (a) $E(X)$
  (b) $Var(X)$
  (c) $P(1 \le X \le 6)$

6 Find the mode and the mean of the distribution which has density function $\dfrac{2}{27}(6 + x - x^2)$ for $0 \le x \le 3$.

7 The probability that a dog will have finished his meal X mins after starting is given by the PDF

  $f(x) = \begin{cases} K(5 - x) & 0 \le x \le 4 \\ 0 & \text{otherwise} \end{cases}$

  Sketch the PDF and find the value of K.

  Find the expected finishing time and the standard deviation.

  If a pack of four dogs begin eating their own meals simultaneously, and independently, what is the probability that they will all have finished by three minutes?

8 The PDF of a random variable X is given by

  $f(x) = \begin{cases} \dfrac{6x}{25} - \dfrac{6x^2}{125} & 0 \le x \le 5 \\ 0 & \text{otherwise} \end{cases}$

  Find $E(X)$.

  The lifetime of X in years of an electric light bulb has this distribution. I buy two such new bulbs and their failures are independent.

  Find the probability that:
  (a) neither bulb fails in the first year
  (b) exactly one bulb fails within two years.

SUMMARY EXERCISE

1 The random variable X has probability density function

$$f(x) = \begin{cases} 10cx^2 & 0 \le x < 0.6 \\ 9c(1 - x) & 0.6 \le x \le 1.0 \\ 0 & \text{otherwise} \end{cases}$$

where c is a constant.

(a) Find the value of c and sketch the graph of the probability density function.

The mode of a random variable X is the value of x for which the probability density function is a maximum.

(b) Write down the mode of X.

(c) Find the probability that X is less than 0.4.

2 The continuous random variable X has probability density function

$$f(x) = \begin{cases} 0 & x \le 0 \\ 6kx(1 - x) & 0 < x < 1 \\ \dfrac{k}{x^2} & x \ge 1 \end{cases}$$

Find k and $P\left(X > \frac{1}{2}\right)$

3 A random variable X has PDF $f(x)$ given by

$$f(x) = \begin{cases} 3x - x^2 & 0 \le x \le 1 \\ \dfrac{1}{2x^2} & x > 1 \end{cases}$$

Find the CDF $F(x)$ and hence find (a) $F\left(\frac{1}{2}\right)$ (b) $F(5)$

4 The length of life X, in years, of a new sort of television tube is modelled by the continuous distribution with cumulative distribution function:

$$F(x) = \begin{cases} 0 & x \le 0 \\ \dfrac{6}{1000}\left(5x^2 - \dfrac{1}{3}x^3\right) & 0 < x < 10 \\ 1 & x \ge 10 \end{cases}$$

(a) Find, and sketch, the probability density function of X.

(b) A small hotel buys 8 television sets for its bedrooms. Find the probability that no tubes fail in the first two years.

(c) I buy a television set, and the tube is still working after two years. Given this information, find the probability that the tube will not fail during the next two years.

(d) Give two reasons why the distribution above is unlikely to be realistic as a model for the distribution of lifetimes of television tubes.   **C** 3.2

5 The random variable X has PDF given by:

$$f(x) = \begin{cases} 0 & x < 0 \\ kx(2 - x) & 0 \le x \le 2 \\ 0 & x > 2 \end{cases}$$

Find:

(a) k

(b) the mode of X

(c) the median of X.

6 The CDF of a random variable X is given by

$$F(x) = \begin{cases} 0 & x < 0 \\ x^5 & 0 \le x \le 1 \\ 1 & x > 1 \end{cases}$$

Find:

(a) the PDF of X

(b) $P(X) \le 0.2)$

(c) the value of n if $P(X \le n) = \frac{1}{32}$

SUMMARY

In this section we have studied continuous random variables. We have seen that:

- a **probability density function (PDF)** of random variable X defined over $a \le x \le b$ is a function $f(x)$ such that

  (a) $\displaystyle\int_a^b f(x)\,dx = 1$ (b) $f(x) \ge 0$ for $a \le x \le b$

- $P(X \le x_0) = \displaystyle\int_a^{x_0} f(x)\,dx$ for $a \le x_0 \le b$

- the **cumulative distribution function (CDF)** of random variable X is given by

  $F(x) = \displaystyle\int_a^x f(t)\,dt$ for $a \le x \le b$

- $P(X \le x_0) = F(x_0)$

- $f(x) = \dfrac{dF(x)}{dx}$

- the **median** Q_2 is such that $= \displaystyle\int_a^{Q_2} f(t)\,dt = 0.5$

- the **lower quartile** Q_1 is such that $= \displaystyle\int_a^{Q_1} f(t)\,dt = 0.25$

- The **upper quartile** Q_3 is such that $= \displaystyle\int_a^{Q_3} f(t)\,dt = 0.75$

- the **mode** of X will be

  either m, where $a < m \le b$, and $f(m)$ is the greatest value of $f(x)$ in the given range

  or   it will be given by solving $f'(x) = 0$ in the given range.

- the **mean** of X is given by

  $E(X) = \displaystyle\int_a^b x f(x)\,dx$

- the **variance** of X is given by

  $Var(X) = \displaystyle\int_a^b x^2 f(x)\,dx - [E(X)]^2$

  i.e. $Var(X) = E(X^2) - [E(X)]^2$

ANSWERS

Practice questions A

1

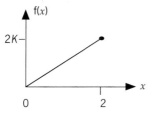

(a) 0.5 (b) 0.36

2

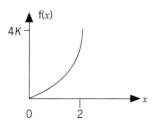

(a) 0.375 (b) 0.027

3

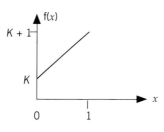

(a) 0.5 (b) 0.88

4

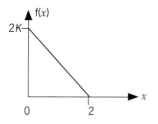

(a) 0.5 (b) 0.64

5

(a) 6 (b) 0.648

6

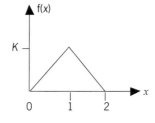

(a) 1 (b) 0.875

7 (a) 4 (b) 1.231

8 (a) 1.5

(b) $= \displaystyle\int_{0.9}^{1} f(x)\, dx = 0.125$

9 $\left(\dfrac{2}{3}\right)^2 = \dfrac{4}{9}$

Practice questions B

1 (a)
$$F(x) = \begin{cases} 0 & x < 0 \\ 0.25x^2 & 0 \le x \le 2 \\ 1 & x \ge 2 \end{cases}$$

(b)
$$F(x) = \begin{cases} 0 & x < 0 \\ \dfrac{x^3}{8} & 0 \le x \le 2 \\ 1 & x \ge 2 \end{cases}$$

(c)
$$F(x) = \begin{cases} 0 & x < 0 \\ \dfrac{1}{2}x + \dfrac{x^2}{2} & 0 \le x \le 1 \\ 1 & x \ge 1 \end{cases}$$

(d)
$$F(x) = \begin{cases} 0 & x < 0 \\ x - \dfrac{x^2}{4} & 0 \le x \le 2 \\ 1 & x \ge 2 \end{cases}$$

(e)
$$F(x) = \begin{cases} 0 & x < 0 \\ 3x^2 - 2x^3 & 0 \le x \le 1 \\ 1 & x \ge 1 \end{cases}$$

2 $\dfrac{1}{8}, \dfrac{1}{2}, \dfrac{7}{8}$

3 (a)
$$f(x) = \begin{cases} \dfrac{1}{8} + \dfrac{3x^2}{8} & 1 \le x \le 2 \\ 0 & \text{otherwise} \end{cases}$$

(b) 0.152

4 (a) 4

(b)
$$F(x) = \begin{cases} 0 & x < 0 \\ x^4 & 0 \le x \le 1 \\ 1 & x > 1 \end{cases}$$

5 (a) -0.5

(b)
$$F(x) = \begin{cases} 0 & x < 0 \\ x - \dfrac{x^2}{4} & 0 \le x \le 2 \\ 1 & x > 2 \end{cases}$$

6 (a)
$$f(x) = \begin{cases} \dfrac{0.5}{\sqrt{x}} & 1 \le x \le 4 \\ 0 & \text{otherwise} \end{cases}$$

(b) $\sqrt{2} - 1 \approx 0.414$

7 (a)
$$f(x) = \begin{cases} \dfrac{1}{3x^2} & 0.2 \le x \le 0.5 \\ 0 & \text{otherwise} \end{cases}$$

(b) $\dfrac{5}{9}$

Practice questions C

1 (a) (i)

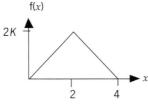

(ii) $\dfrac{1}{4}$ (iii) 2 (by inspection)

(b) (i)

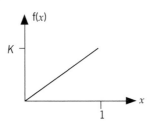

(ii) 2   (iii) 1 (by inspection)

(c) (i)

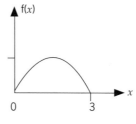

(ii) $\dfrac{2}{9}$ (iii) 1.5 (by symmetry)

(d) (i)

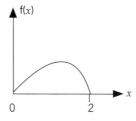

(ii) $\dfrac{3}{4}$ (iii) $1\dfrac{1}{3}$ (by differentiation)

2

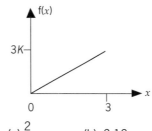

(a) $\dfrac{2}{9}$ (b) 2.12

3 0.794

4 (a) 1.682   (b) 1.414
(c) 1.861   (d) 0.447 ; 2

5 2

6

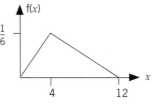

0.542, 4 and 5.07

7

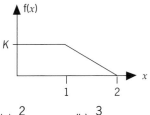

(a) $\frac{2}{3}$ (b) $\frac{3}{4}$

Practice questions D

1 (a) (i)

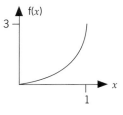

(ii) $\frac{3}{4}$

(iii) 0.0375

(b) (i)

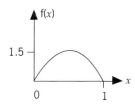

(ii) 0.5 (by symmetry)

(iii) 0.05

(c) (i)

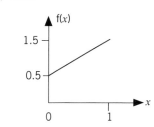

(ii) $\frac{7}{12}$

(iii) 0.0764

(d) (i)

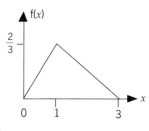

(ii) $\frac{4}{3}$ (iii) 0.389

2 2.5, 0.185

3 (a) 2.4

(b) 1.44

(c) 2

4

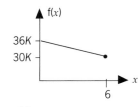

$2\frac{10}{11}$, 0.154

5

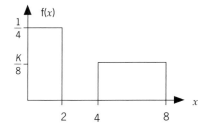

$k = 1$

(a) 3.5

(b) 7.083

(c) 0.5

6 $\frac{1}{2}$, $1\frac{1}{6}$

7

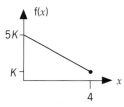

$K = \frac{1}{12}$, $E(X) = 1.56$,

standard deviation $= \sqrt{1.12} = 1.06$

$\left(\frac{7}{8}\right)^4$

8 $E(X) = 2\frac{1}{2}$

(a) 0.803

(b) 0.456

3

Continuous distributions

In Unit S1 we studied that most important of *continuous* distributions – the normal distribution. In this section we are going to look at another *exact* continuous distribution, as well as two *approximate* normal distributions.

The exact continuous distribution will be the continuous uniform distribution – a continuous version of the discrete distribution studied in unit S1. This will require some integration so, if you need some revision, now is the time to look back at the relevant sections in unit P1.

As for the approximate normal distributions we'll see how, in certain circumstances, both the binomial and Poisson distributions become approximately normal – even though the former pair are discrete and the normal distribution is continuous. Once again the versatility of the normal distribution shines through!

The continuous uniform distribution

OCR S3 5.13.1 (a)

The **continuous uniform distribution** is defined as follows:

> Random variable X has a distribution which is uniform in the interval
>
> $$a \leq x \leq b \text{ if:}$$
>
> $$f(x) = \begin{cases} \dfrac{1}{b-a} & \text{for } a \leq x \leq b \\ 0 & \text{otherwise} \end{cases}$$

We write $X \sim U(a, b)$ if X is a random variable with a continuous uniform distribution.

The PDF of X is shown in Fig. 3.1.

Figure 3.1

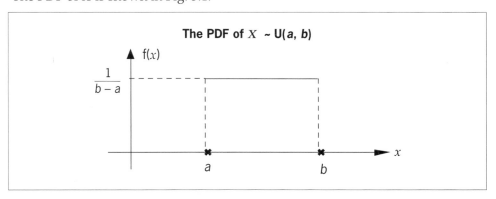

The PDF of $X \sim U(a, b)$

Note that the basic requirement for a PDF is satisfied since the area under the 'curve' is:

$$(b - a) \times \frac{1}{(b - a)} = 1$$

The cumulative distribution function for $X \sim U(a, b)$

With the usual notation, $F(x)$ is represented by the shaded area in Fig. 3.2.

Figure 3.2

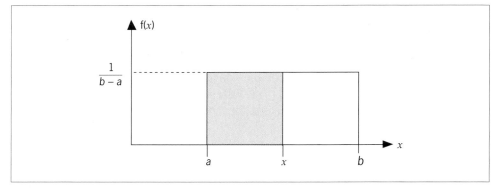

$$\therefore \; F(x) = (x - a) \times \frac{1}{(b - a)} \qquad \Rightarrow \qquad F(x) = \frac{x - a}{b - a}$$

In full, this can be written:

$$F(x) = \begin{cases} 0 & x < a \\ \dfrac{x - a}{b - a} & a \leq x \leq b \\ 1 & x > b \end{cases}$$

The mean and variance of $X \sim U(a, b)$

It is clear that *the mean of X is mid-way between a and b*

$$\therefore \; E(X) = \frac{a + b}{2}$$

As far as *the variance* is concerned it is probably easier to use the alternative definition

$$\text{Var}(X) = \int_a^b (x - \overline{x})^2 \, f(x) \, dx$$

so that, for $X \sim U(a, b)$ we get

$$\text{Var}(X) = \int_a^b (x - \overline{x})^2 \, K \, dx \; \left(\text{where } \overline{x} = \frac{a + b}{2} \text{ and } K = \frac{1}{b - a} \right)$$

$$= K \int_a^b (x - \overline{x})^2 \, dx$$

$$= K \left[\frac{(x - \overline{x})^3}{3} \right]_a^b$$

$$= \frac{K}{3} \left\{ (b - \bar{x})^3 - (a - \bar{x})^3 \right\}$$

$$= \frac{K}{3} \left\{ \left(\frac{b-a}{2}\right)^3 - \left(\frac{a-b}{2}\right)^3 \right\} \quad \left(\text{since } \bar{x} = \frac{a+b}{2}\right)$$

$$= \frac{K}{3} \left\{ \frac{(b-a)^3}{8} + \frac{(b-a)^3}{8} \right\}$$

$$= \frac{K}{12}(b-a)^3 = \frac{(b-a)^2}{12} \quad \left(\text{since } K = \frac{1}{b-a}\right)$$

In summary then:

> If $\quad X \sim U(a, b)$
>
> then $\quad E(X) = \dfrac{a + b}{2}$
>
> and $\quad \text{Var}(X) = \dfrac{(b-a)^2}{12}$

Your syllabus 'includes the derivation of the mean and variance of a continuous uniform distribution' and so *you may well be expected to reproduce the above.* However, if a question says 'write down the mean and variance of a continuous uniform distribution' then *you need only quote the formulae above.*

Example   If $X \sim U(5, 11)$, write down the values of $E(X)$ and $\text{Var}(X)$.

Solution   Here $a = 5$ and $b = 11$

$$\therefore \quad E(X) \quad = \frac{5 + 11}{2} = 8$$

$$\therefore \quad \text{Var}(X) \quad = \frac{(11 - 5)^2}{12} = 3$$

Example   If $X \sim U(-1, 7)$, derive the values of $E(X)$ and $\text{Var}(X)$.

Solution

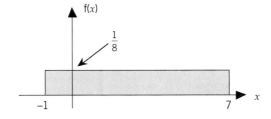

By symmetry $E(X)$ is midway between -1 and 7

$$\therefore \quad E(X) = \frac{-1 + 7}{2} = 3.$$

Also $E(X^2)$ $= \int_{-1}^{7} x^2 \frac{1}{8} \, dx = \frac{1}{8} \int_{-1}^{7} x^2 \, dx = \frac{1}{8} \left[\frac{x^3}{3} \right]_{-1}^{7} = 14\frac{1}{3}$

$\therefore \text{Var}(X) = E(X^2) - \left[E(X) \right]^2 = 14\frac{1}{3} - 3^2 = 5\frac{1}{3}$

$\left(\text{This is confirmed by } \frac{(b-a)^2}{12} = \frac{(7+1)^2}{12} = 5\frac{1}{3} \right)$

An *alternative method* for variance would be as follows:

$$\text{Var}(X) = \int_{-1}^{7} (x - \bar{x})^2 \frac{1}{8} \, dx$$

$$= \frac{1}{8} \int_{-1}^{7} (x - 3)^2 \, dx$$

$$= \left[\frac{(x-3)^3}{24} \right]_{-1}^{7}$$

$$= 5\frac{1}{3}$$

The choice is yours!

Practice questions A

1 The random variable X has PDF given by

$$f(x) = \begin{cases} K & 1 \leq x \leq 3 \\ 0 & \text{otherwise} \end{cases}$$

Illustrate with a sketch and find the value of K.

If four randomly chosen values of X are taken, what is the probability that 3 of them are less than $1\frac{1}{2}$?

2 A variate X can assume any value between 2 and 4 and its PDF is given by

$$f(x) = \begin{cases} K & 2 \leq x \leq 4 \\ 0 & \text{otherwise} \end{cases}$$

Sketch the distribution and state the value of K. Find the mean and variance (i.e. quote the formulae if you wish).

3 The continuous variate X has a uniform distribution over its range 0 to 12. Write down the mean and median. Calculate the variance of X (i.e. don't quote the formula for Var X – work it out from the definition).

4 If $X \sim U(2, 8)$ find $E(X)$, $E(X^2)$ and Var (X).

5 A random variable X has a PDF given by

$$f(x) = \begin{cases} K & -4 \leq x \leq -2 \\ K & 2 \leq x \leq 4 \\ 0 & \text{otherwise} \end{cases}$$

(a) Sketch the distribution.

(b) Find the value of K.

(c) Find $E(X)$.

(d) Find the standard deviation of X.

(e) Find the probability of obtaining a value of X within one standard deviation of the mean.

6 If $X \sim U(1, 9)$ write down the values of $E(X)$ and Var(X).

Find the CDF $F(x)$.

Find the median, lower quartile, upper quartile and interquartile range.

Using the normal distribution to approximate the binomial and Poisson distributions

Just as we can, under certain conditions ($n > 50$, $p < 0.1$), use the Poisson distribution to approximate the binomial distribution, so we can use the normal distribution to approximate the binomial and Poisson distributions.

Normal approximation to the binomial distribution

OCR S2 5.12.2 (c)

Recall that if X is a binomial random variable with parameters n and p $\big($i.e. $X \sim B(n, p)\big)$ then $E(X) = np$, $\text{Var}(X) = np\,(1 - p)$

Now if $np > 5$ and $n(1 - p) > 5$, the binomial distribution can be approximated by a normal distribution having the same mean and variance.

i.e. $X \sim B(n, p) \Rightarrow X \approx N\big(np, np\,(1 - p)\big)$

where $\approx$ means 'is approximately distributed'.

Now, the binomial distribution is discrete and the normal distribution is continuous so better approximations are obtained using a continuity correction.

We now illustrate this with an example.

Example

X is the number of heads obtained when a coin is tossed 20 times. Find:

(a) $P(X \leq 13)$

(b) $P(X < 13)$

(c) $P(X > 13)$

(d) $P(X \geq 13)$

(e) $P(X = 13)$

For part (e), we will also check the accuracy of the result.

Solution

We could obtain each of these probabilities using the exact distribution, i.e. $X \sim B(20, \frac{1}{2})$. However, this would be a laborious calculation:

$$P(X \leq 13) = P(X = 0) + P(X = 1) + (P(X = 2) + \dots + P(X = 13)$$

Fortunately, we can get very close to the correct answer by using the normal approximation.

Firstly note that:

$$X \sim B(20, \tfrac{1}{2}) \ \Rightarrow X \approx N\big(20 \times \tfrac{1}{2},\ 20 \times \tfrac{1}{2} \times \tfrac{1}{2}\big)$$

i.e. $X \approx N(10, 5)$

and that the parameters of the binomial distribution are suitable for such an approximation to be made because $np = 10 > 5$ and $n(1 - p) = 10 > 5$.

(a) $P(X \leq 13)$

Look at Fig. 3.3.

Figure 3.3

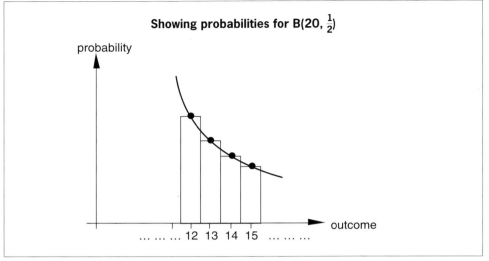

Showing probabilities for B(20, $\frac{1}{2}$)

Figure 3.2 shows how calculating a binomial probability amounts to adding up chunks of discrete probability. The curve which approximates these, as shown in the diagram, would pass through the mid-points of the tops of the bars and finding $P(X \leq 13)$ from the curve would miss half of the bar for $X = 13$.

For this reason we apply a continuity correction and find $P(X \leq 13.5)$ as it will give a better approximation than would finding $P(X \leq 13)$.

The problem now is:

for the distribution $X \approx N(10, 5)$ find $P(X \leq 13.5)$

Let $Z = \dfrac{X - 10}{\sqrt{5}}$ then $Z \sim N(0, 1)$ (See S1 if you've forgotten this!)

$P(X \leq 13.5) = P\left(Z \leq \dfrac{13.5 - 10}{\sqrt{5}}\right)$

$= P(Z \leq 1.57)$

$= 0.9418$ (from the tables in Appendix 3, see p. 71)

Hence $P(13$ or less heads$) \approx 0.94$ (2 d.p.)

(The correct answer to 4 d.p. is 0.9423 and so the approximation is exact to 2 d.p.)

(b) $P(X < 13)$

Now the first step is to write $P(X \leq 12)$ which, in a discrete distribution, is the same and then we can use the approximating distribution $X \sim N(10, 5)$ and find $P(X \leq 12.5)$.

$\therefore \quad P(X \leq 12.5) = P\left(Z \leq \dfrac{12.5 - 10}{\sqrt{5}}\right) = P(Z \leq 1.12)$

$= 0.8686$ (from the tables)

So $P(\text{less than 13 trials}) = 0.87$ (2 d.p.)

(c) $P(X > 13)$

$= 1 - P(X \leq 13)$

$\approx 1 - P(X \leq 13.5)$ (using continuity correction)

$= 1 - 0.94 \ \left(\text{using (a)}\right)$

$= 0.06$

i.e. P(more than 13 heads) ≈ 0.06

(d) $P(X \geq 13)$

$= 1 - P(X \leq 12)$

$\approx 1 - P(X \leq 12.5)$ (using continuity correction)

$= 1 - 0.87 \ \left(\text{using (b)}\right)$

$= 0.13$

i.e. P(13 or more heads) ≈ 0.13

(e) For $P(X = 13)$ using a normal approximation directly would give a zero answer since for any continuous distribution the probability of an individual outcome is always zero.

To get round this problem we could approximate $P(X = 13)$ by $P(12.5 \leq X \leq 13.5)$

i.e. use a continuity correction in both directions.

But: $\quad P(12.5 \leq X \leq 13.5)$ for $X \approx N(10, 5)$ gives

$$P\left(\frac{12.5 - 10}{\sqrt{5}} \leq Z \leq \frac{13.5 - 10}{\sqrt{5}} \right)$$

$= P(1.12 \leq Z \leq 1.57)$

$= 0.9418 - 0.8686 = 0.07 \ (2 \text{ d.p.})$

The exact answer is $\binom{20}{13} \left(\frac{1}{2}\right)^{13} \left(\frac{1}{2}\right)^{7} = 0.0739 \ (4 \text{ d.p.})$

so the approximation is good.

In conclusion if we have $X \sim B\,(n, p)$ and we wish to find $P(X \leq x)$

by using a normal approximation, then we use the distribution

$$X \approx N(np, np\,(1 - p))$$

and find $P\left(X \leq x + \frac{1}{2}\right)$ using a continuity correction.

The approximation is appropriate for $np > 5$ and $nq > 5$ (where $q = 1 - p$).

Note: We saw in the last example that *all* discrete probabilities can be re-formulated to be given in terms of probabilities in the required form $P(X \leq x)$ and this should always be the first step.

Practice questions B

1 A poll indicates that 40% of the UK are Labour supporters.

(a) A random group of 100 people is chosen. Use an approximate normal distribution to estimate the probability of at least 43 Labour supporters.

(b) Justify your use of the normal approximation. **C** 3.2

2 85% of pupils still have their original calculators.

(a) A random group of 100 pupils is chosen. Use an approximate normal distribution to estimate the probability of no more than 80 of the group still having their original calculators.

(b) Justify your use of the normal approximation. **C** 3.2

3 42% of eggs are bad.

You buy 600 eggs and want to work out the probability that no more than 240 of them are bad.

(a) Justify using a normal approximation. **C** 3.2

(b) Answer the question.

4 It is known that 1 in 5 people watched The Grand National on TV last year.

(a) A random group of 100 people is chosen. Use a normal approximation to estimate the probability that more than 30 of them watched The Grand National

(b) Justify your use of the normal approximation. **C** 3.2

5 The probability a silicon chip fails is 0.3

(a) A random sample of 100 silicon chips is chosen. Use an approximate normal distribution to estimate the probability of less than 60 working (i.e. more than 40 failures).

(b) Justify your use of the normal approximation. **C** 3.2

6 If $X \sim B(200, 0.7)$, use the normal approximation to find:

(a) $P(X \geq 130)$

(b) $P(X > 152)$

7 Another poll suggests that one in three of the UK population are Conservative supporters.

(a) You choose a random sample of 9 people and X is the number that are Conservative supporters. State an assumption that has to be made for X to be modelled on a binomial distribution.

Assuming a binomial model, what is the expected number of Conservative supporters in the group? What is the probability of getting that expected number?

(b) A random sample of 162 people is now chosen. Use a normal approximation to estimate the probability that the group contains no more than 52 Conservative supporters. Justify your use of the normal model. **C** 3.2

8 The lifetimes of bulbs are normally distributed with mean 800 hours and standard deviation 10 hours. A bulb is acceptable if its lifetime lies between 775 hours and 818 hours.

(a) What proportion of bulbs are 'acceptable'?

(b) 3 bulbs are now chosen and X is the number that is 'acceptable'. State an assumption for X to be modelled on a binomial distribution and hence find the probability that exactly 2 of them are 'acceptable'.

(c) If a bulb has a lifetime between 800 hours and 810 hours, it is said to be 'average'.

What proportion of bulbs are 'average'?

(d) 100 bulbs are now chosen and Y is the number that are 'average'. Assuming that Y can be modelled by a binomial distribution, state the values of $E(Y)$ and $Var(Y)$.

Explain why Y is approximately normally distributed and hence estimate the probability that less than 30 of this group are 'average'. **C** 3.2

Normal approximation to Poisson `OCR S2 5.12.3 (e)`

If $X \sim P(\mu)$ and μ is large (say, $\mu > 10$), then we can find approximate values for the Poisson probabilities by using a normal distribution with the same mean and variance, and by using a continuity correction (since we are again approximating a discrete distribution by a continuous one).

The result is:

if $X \sim P(\mu)$ then $X \approx N(\mu, \mu)$

provided μ is sufficiently large ($\mu > 10$ will give reasonable approximations)

Example	If $X \sim P(15)$ find $P(X > 21)$ by using a normal approximation.

Solution	To apply the normal approximation, we will write $P(X > 21)$ as $1 - P(X \leq 21)$. We apply the continuity correction to this so that we work out:

$$1 - P(X \leq 21.5)$$

from the distribution N(15, 15)

Let $\quad Z = \dfrac{X - 15}{\sqrt{15}}$

Then $\quad P(X \leq 21.5) = P\left(Z \leq \dfrac{21.5 - 15}{\sqrt{15}}\right)$

$\qquad\qquad\qquad\quad = P(Z \leq 1.68) = 0.9535$ (from tables)

So $\quad 1 - P(X \leq 21.5) \quad = 0.0465 \approx 0.05$ (2 d.p.)

(The correct answer to 2 d.p. is also 0.05, so the approximation is exact to 2 d.p.)

> In conclusion, if $X \sim P(\mu)$ and $\mu > 10$, to find $P(X \leq r)$,
>
> the approximating distribution $X \approx N(\mu, \mu)$ can be used
>
> and increased accuracy will be obtained by using the continuity correction
> and finding $P(X \leq r + \frac{1}{2})$.

Practice questions C

1   The number of telephone calls per day follows a Poisson distribution with mean 2

   (a) What is the expected number of calls in 8 days?

   (b) Use an approximate normal distribution to estimate the probability in 8 days of

      (i)   at least 17 calls

      (ii) between 10 and 15 calls inclusive

2   The mean number of accidents per week is 3 and the distribution can be assumed to be Poisson.

   Use a normal approximation over 12 weeks to estimate the probability of

   (a) at least 39 accidents

   (b) fewer than 28 accidents

3 The number of fox sightings in a garden in a year is assumed to follow a Poisson distribution with mean 2.

(a) For 2 years find the probability of no more than 5 sightings

(b) For 18 years, use a suitable approximation to estimate the probability of at least 39 sightings.

4 The number of eggs per clutch laid by a tortoise follows a Poisson distribution with mean 3. Use a suitable approximation to estimate the probability of more than 38 eggs in 12 clutches.

5 We expect an average of 1.5 spelling mistakes on a page of newsprint. Use a normal approximation to estimate the probability of more than 32 spelling mistakes in a newspaper of 24 pages.

6 The number of errors in a computer print-out follow a Poisson distribution with a mean of 2 in every 10^5 characters. Using a suitable approximation, estimate the probability of less than 12 errors in a computer print-out of one million characters.

7 In an experiment with a radioactive substance the number of particles reaching a counter over a given period of time follow a Poisson distribution with mean 22. Estimate the probability that the number of particles reaching the counter over the given period of time is 18 or more.

8 The number of eggs laid by a chicken averages 200 a year and follows a Poisson distribution. Estimate the probability of a chicken laying between 180 and 240 eggs inclusive over the year.

The probability that an egg is fertile is 0.1. What is the expected number of fertile eggs laid by a chicken?

State the distribution that models the number of fertile eggs. Estimate the probability that more than 30 eggs are fertile.

9 On a walk from Holt to the village of Hempstead, the number of rabbit sightings follows a Poisson distribution with mean 6. On such a walk, what is the probability of seeing between 4 and 7 rabbits inclusive?

On the return journey from Hempstead to Holt, the number of rabbits sightings follows a Poisson distribution with mean 7.

If X is the number of rabbit sightings on the Holt→Hempstead→Holt walk, what is the distribution of X? State the mean and variance of X.

Using an approximate normal distribution, which you should justify, estimate the probability of sighting no more than 9 rabbits on the complete walk. **C** 3.2

SUMMARY EXERCISE

1 $X \sim U(-1, 3)$.

For this distribution find $E(X)$, $Var(X)$, $P(X > 0)$, $F(X)$,

and sketch the PDF and CDF.

2 $X \sim B(200, 0.45)$

Find approximations (using continuity correction) to the following:

(a) $P(X \leq 76)$

(b) $P(X > 110)$

(c) $P(80 \leq X < 100)$

3 40% of males need glasses.

(a) Choose a sample of 7 males.
Find P(more than 3 need glasses).

(b) Choose a sample of 700 males.
Find P(more than 300 need glasses).

4 If $X \sim P(14)$, explain why X is approximately normally distributed.

Estimate $P(X > 16)$. **C** 3.2

5 If $X \sim P(20)$, use an approximate normal distribution to estimate the value of n if $P(X < n) = 0.89$.

SUMMARY

In this section we have seen that a **continuous uniform distribution** $X \sim U(a, b)$ has:

- a PDF $f(x)$ given by

$$f(x) = \begin{cases} \dfrac{1}{b-a} & a \leq x \leq b \\ 0 & \text{otherwise} \end{cases}$$

- $E(X) = \dfrac{a+b}{2}$

- $Var(X) = \dfrac{(b-a)^2}{12}$

- a CDF $F(x)$ given by

$$F(x) = \begin{cases} 0 & x < a \\ \dfrac{x-a}{b-a} & a \leq x \leq b \\ 1 & x \geq b \end{cases}$$

We have also seen that a binomial variate $X \sim B(n, p)$ **is approximately normal if**

- $np > 5$ and $nq > 5$ (where $q = 1 - p$)

  In which case we use

- $X \approx N(np, npq)$

  and replace

- $P(X \leq x)$ by the continuity correction $P(X \leq x + \frac{1}{2})$

Furthermore, a Poisson variate $X \sim P(\mu)$ **is approximately normal if**

- $\mu > 10$

  In which case we use

- $X \approx N(\mu, \mu)$

  and replace

- $P(X \leq x)$ by the continuity correction $P(X \leq x + \frac{1}{2})$

ANSWERS

Practice questions A

1

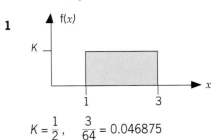

$$K = \frac{1}{2}, \quad \frac{3}{64} = 0.046875$$

2

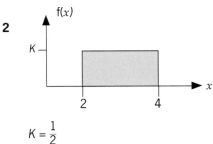

$$K = \frac{1}{2}$$

$$E(X) = 3, \quad Var(X) = \frac{1}{3}$$

3 $E(X) = 6$, median = 6

$$\text{Var } X = \int_0^{12} (x-6)^2 \frac{1}{12} \, dx = \left[\frac{(x-6)^3}{36} \right]_0^{12} = 12$$

4 $E(X) = 5$, $E(X^2) = \int_2^8 \frac{x^2}{6} \, dx = 28$, $\text{Var}(X) = 3$

5 (a)

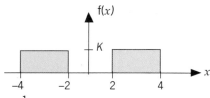

(b) $\frac{1}{4}$

(c) 0

(d) $\sqrt{9\frac{1}{3}} = 3.055$

(e) $\left(\frac{\sqrt{9\frac{1}{3}} - 2}{2} \right) = 0.528$

6 $E(X) = 5$, $\text{Var}(X) = 5\frac{1}{3}$

$$F(x) = \begin{cases} 0 & x < 1 \\ \dfrac{x-1}{8} & 1 \le x \le 9 \\ 1 & x > 9 \end{cases}$$

median = 5, $Q_1 = 3$, $Q_3 = 7$, I.R = 4

Practice questions B

1 (a) 0.305 (b) 40 > 5, 60 > 5

2 (a) 0.1038 (b) 85 > 5, 15 > 5

3 (a) 252 > 5, 348 > 5 (b) 0.171

4 (a) 0.00436 (b) 20 > 5, 80 > 5

5 (a) 0.011 (b) 30 > 5, 70 > 5

6 (a) 0.9474 (b) 0.0269

7 (a) Each of the 9 has a $\frac{1}{3}$ probability of being a
Conservative supporter
3, 0.273

(b) 0.4013. Valid since 54 > 5, 108 > 5

8 (a) 0.9579

(b) Each of the 3 bulbs has a probability of 0.9579
of being 'acceptable'. Final answer = 0.116.

(c) 0.3413

(d) $E(Y) = 34.13$, $\text{Var}(Y) = 22.48$
34.13 > 5 and 65.87 > 5
0.165

Practice questions C

1 (a) 16 (b) (i) 0.4502 (ii) 0.3981

2 (a) 0.3384 (b) 0.0783

3 (a) $X \sim P(4)$ $\therefore$ 0.7851
(b) $X \approx N(36, 36)$ $\therefore$ 0.3385

4 0.3385

5 0.72

6 0.0287

7 0.8312

8 0.92441, 20, $X \sim P(20)$, 0.00944

9 0.593, $X \sim P(13)$ and $E(X) = \text{Var}(X) = 13$,
0.1657, valid because 13 > 10.

SECTION

4

Hypothesis tests

INTRODUCTION   In this section we are going to check out the validity of some binomial and Poisson models. For example, suppose it is claimed that 40% of teenagers watch *Top of the Pops*, yet when you ask a sample of 14 teenagers, only two of them watched it. Does this suggest that the claim is wrong? Then again, it is claimed that goals scored by football teams follow a Poisson distribution with mean 1.2. Yet, when you checked out the scores of a sample of 20 teams, you got a mean of 1.5. Does this suggest that the claim is an underestimate?

In this section we'll see how to answer questions such as these.

Testing a theory involving proportions

OCR S2 5.12.4 (a),(g),(h)

Suppose you have a theory that 60% of the families in the UK have at least one pet. How would you go about testing that theory?

One method would be to ask *every family* in the UK whether or not they have a pet. You would refer to that as **taking a census**. It would be difficult to carry out and would take a very long time. Even its accuracy would be doubtful because you couldn't guarantee that you'd be able to find every family and, even then, they wouldn't necessarily tell you the truth, or even answer the question!

Alternatively you could **take a sample** of UK families. This would be quicker than a census, but its accuracy would depend on how representative the sample was. (In unit S3, we'll study the various types of samples that could be taken, but for unit S2 we need only the idea of a sample.)

In either case you would have to begin by numbering all the families in the UK as 1, 2, 3, … ! This would be your **sampling frame**. An individual family in your sampling frame would be a **sampling unit**.

Let's suppose, then, by some method or other, you've got some results from UK families and 64% of them had at least one pet. Does this disprove your theory of 60%? Not really, the difference could just be due to sampling error. What about 68%, 74%, 78%, 80% … ? Where do we draw the line and say, ah!, my theory isn't correct?

Let's set the question in a formal way, and then we can work through to the solution.

| Example | I think that 60% of UK families have at least one pet. I sample 12 families and 9 of them have at least one pet. Am I underestimating the number of pet owners? |

| Solution | First of all we set up two hypotheses. The **null hypothesis** is one which states that no change has taken place. The symbol for null hypothesis is H_0 so in this example we write: |

H_0: $p = 0.6$

(i.e. the proportion of pet owners is 0.6).

The **alternative hypothesis** (AH) is one which predicts that a change has taken place. In this example, because of the key word 'underestimating' in the wording of the problem, the appropriate statement is:

AH: $p > 0.6$

(i.e. the alternative hypothesis is that more than 60% are pet owners.)

The object of the exercise (hypothesis test) is now to determine which of H_0 and AH is the more valid, given the information that we have. As with all situations in statistics, we can never have absolute certainty – only a degree of confidence.

What we now have to decide is at what point would we consider the **observed value** to be so large as to invalidate the theory that $p = 0.6$. We need to decide on the value of x in Fig. 4.1.

| **Figure 4.1** | 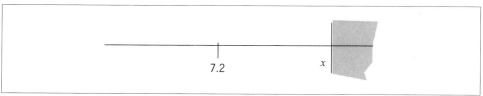 |

(If 60% is correct, then a sample of 12 should give an expected value of 7.2 as pet owners. Hence I've marked 7.2 on the line above.)

This is a decision problem, and a commonly used measure is to have a percentage of 5% to the right of x. This is referred to as a **5% significance level**.

We now have the situation shown in Fig. 4.2.

| **Figure 4.2** | 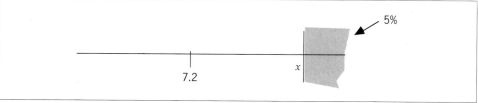 |

So then, does our observed value of 9 (out of 12) fall in the shaded area? Assuming that H_0 is true,

$$P(x \geq 9) \quad = P(x = 9 \text{ or } 10 \text{ or } 11 \text{ or } 12)$$
$$= \binom{12}{9}(0.6)^9(0.4)^3 + \binom{12}{10}(0.6)^{10}(0.4)^2 + \binom{12}{11}(0.6)^{11}(0.4) + (0.6)^{12}$$
$$= 0.2253$$

i.e. there is a 22.53% chance of getting an observed value of 9 or more.

This is well outside the shaded area and so we accept H_0 as being true.

The observed value of 9 is called a **test statistic** and the shaded area is called the **critical region** (the unshaded area is called the **acceptance region**). This is summarised in Fig. 4.3.

Figure 4.3

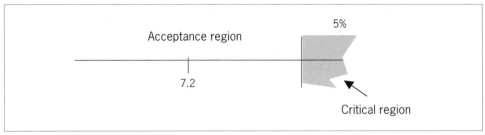

If the observed value falls in the acceptance region then we accept H_0. If it falls in the critical region we accept AH. In our example, 9 fell in the acceptance region and hence we accepted H_0, i.e. we accept that my 60% claim is correct.

You will probably find this a bit tricky to begin with, so let's try one more example.

Example

A gardener sows 12 cabbage seeds and finds that 6 germinate. Test whether the germination rate is less than 75%. Use a 5% level of significance.

Solution

H_0 : $\quad p = 0.75$

AH : $\quad p < 0.75$

(the crucial phrase in the question is *less than 75%*.)

Our sample was 12 and so, if H_0 is true, we would expect 9 to germinate (see Fig. 4.4).

Figure 4.4

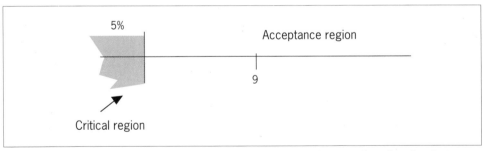

We now see whether or not our sample reading of 6 falls within the shaded area.

$$\therefore \quad P(x \leq 6) \quad = P(0, 1, 2, 3, 4, 5 \text{ or } 6)$$
$$= (0.25)^{12} + \binom{12}{1} (0.25)^{11} (0.75) + \binom{12}{2} (0.25)^{10} (0.75)^2$$
$$+ \binom{12}{3} (0.25)^9 (0.75)^3 + \binom{12}{4} (0.25)^8 (0.75)^4$$
$$+ \binom{12}{5} (0.25)^7 (0.75)^5 + \binom{12}{6} (0.25)^6 (0.75)^6$$
$$= 0.0544$$

i.e. there is a 5.44% chance of getting 6 or less. This is *just* within the acceptance region and so we must accept H_0 and say that the germination rate is 75%. (However, it is so close to the critical region that a further sample is recommended!)

Practice questions A

C 3.2

1 State H_0 and AH in the following cases:

(a) I think 35% of cats have fleas.
Mary thinks the figure is less than that.

(b) A manufacturer claims that 15% are 'everlasting'. I think it is more than that.

(c) A firm producing headache pills claims 70% success. A rival firm claim a higher success rate.

(d) A seed merchant claims 90% germination. I think the rate is less.

(e) A lettuce supplier claims 75% are bug-free. I don't agree (be careful!).

2 (a) I think that 35% of cats have fleas. Mary thinks it is less than that. A sample of 14 cats had 2 with fleas. Test my theory at the 5% level of significance.

(b) A manufacturer claims that 15% are everlasting. I think it is more than that. A sample of 14 had 5 which were everlasting. Test the manufacturer's claim at the 5% level of significance.

(c) A firm producing headache pills claims 70% success. A rival firm claims a higher success rate. A sample of 12 of the rivals pills cured 11 headaches. Test the claims at the 5% level of significance.

(d) A seed merchant claims 90% germination. I think it is less. A sample of 14 seeds had 10 which germinated. Test the claim at the 5% level of significance.

3 A coin is thrown 8 times and 7 heads are obtained. Test, at the 5% level of significance, whether there is evidence of bias towards heads.

4 A coin is thrown 12 times and 9 heads are obtained. Test, at the 5% level of significance, whether there is evidence of bias towards heads.

5 In a survey it was found that 3 out of 10 people supported fox hunting. A month later Jim asked 5 people for their views and 2 were in favour of fox hunting. At the 5% level of significance, is there evidence that support for fox hunting has increased?

6 It is thought that $X \sim B(9, \frac{1}{3})$. A single observation of X gave 6. Is there evidence at the 5% level of significance that $p > \frac{1}{3}$?

7 The manufacturer of a new type of seeding compost claims that seeds sown in the new compost will have a higher rate of germination than if they were sown in ordinary compost. For the particular variety of seed sown in ordinary compost it is known that the germination rate is 0.7. To test the manufacturer's claim, an experiment was conducted in which 20 of the seeds were sown in the new compost and it was found that 18 of them germinated. Assuming a 5% significance level, determine whether the experimental evidence is strong enough to support the claim.

8 The makers of the washing-up liquid 'Shine' claim that 35% of all people use their product, whereas this figure is disputed by a competitor as being an overestimate. In a random sample of 12 people it was found that 2 of them used 'Shine'. Use a 10% significance level to test the claim made by the makers of 'Shine' against the claim made by the competitor.

One-tailed and two-tailed tests

OCR S2 5.12.4 (g)

Tests of the form
$$H_0 : \quad p = k$$
$$AH : \quad p > k \text{ (here we are looking for an increase in } p)$$

or
$$H_0 : \quad p = k$$
$$AH : \quad p < k \text{ (looking for a decrease)}$$

are referred to as **one-tailed tests** since the critical region lies at just one end of the distribution.

Tests of the form $H_0 : \quad p = k$
$\qquad\qquad\qquad$ AH : $\quad p \neq k$ (looking for a change)

are referred to as **two-tailed tests** and here the critical region is split into two, e.g. at a 5% level of significance there would be $2\frac{1}{2}\%$ at each end of the distribution. It is important when conducting hypothesis tests that the hypothesis, the nature of the test, and the significance levels, are decided before any data are actually collected.

Example

A lettuce supplier claims that 75% are bug-free. I don't agree. I purchased 16 of his lettuces and found that 8 were bug-free. Test the claim at the 6% level of significance.

Solution

First we need to establish the hypotheses. The critical words in the problem are 'don't agree'. We are not asked to test whether there are more or less, but whether it is simply different. This implies a two-tailed test and two hypotheses such that:

$H_0 : \qquad p = 0.75$
$AH : \qquad p \neq 0.75$

Now, since the level of significance was 6%, we get the situation shown in Fig. 4.5.

Figure 4.5

(the tails share the 6% equally – 3% each and the expected value from our sample of 16 would be 12 if H_0 were correct.)

The sample reading was 8 (out of 16) and so we need to *see whether this 8 falls within the left-hand tail*.

(It can't be in the right-hand tail because that is bigger than 12.)

$$\therefore \quad P(x \leq 8) \quad = \quad P(0, 1, 2, 3, 4, 5, 6, 7 \text{ or } 8)$$
$$= \quad (0.25)^{16} + \binom{16}{1}(0.25)^{15}(0.75) + \binom{16}{2}(0.25)^{14}(0.75)^2$$
$$+ \quad \binom{16}{3}(0.25)^{13}(0.75)^3 + \binom{16}{4}(0.25)^{12}(0.75)^4$$
$$+ \quad \binom{16}{5}(0.25)^{11}(0.75)^5 + \binom{16}{6}(0.25)^{10}(0.75)^6$$
$$+ \quad \binom{16}{7}(0.25)^{9}(0.75)^7 + \binom{16}{8}(0.25)^{8}(0.75)^8$$
$$= \quad 0.0271$$

i.e. there is a chance of 2.71% of getting 8 or less. This is within the left tail and so we accept AH.

$\therefore \quad p \neq 0.75$

$\therefore$ The number of bug-free lettuce is different from 75%.

Practice questions B

 C 3.2

1 A coin is thrown 8 times and 6 tails are recorded. Assuming a binomial model and using a 2-tail test at the 5% level of significance, decide whether or not you are surprised by these results.

Would your decision change if 7 tails were recorded?

2 It is suspected that a cheap, imported die is biased. In 15 throws of the die, a 6 occurred once only. Use a 5% level of significance to determine whether this information provides sufficient evidence to uphold the claim.

3 A coin is so damaged that it is not possible to judge whether the probability of a head is equal to, less than, or greater than $\frac{1}{2}$. In 10 throws of the coin a head was obtained 8 times. Test the unbiasedness of the coin, using a 5% significance level.

4 A garage owner claims that the purchase of cars with faulty brakes is different this year from last. Last year 20% had faulty brakes but this year, out of a sample of 18 cars, 8 had faulty brakes. Is there evidence at the 4% level of significance to support the garage owner's claim?

Using cumulative binomial tables

OCR S1 5.11.4 (c)

We have seen that some of the calculations in these hypothesis tests are rather long (to say the least!). Your syllabus does indicate that in *some questions you will be expected to use* **cumulative binomial tables** rather than work the sums out longhand. They'll expect you to do the shorter sums longhand but, for longer ones, be prepared to use the cumulative tables (see Appendix 1, p. 69). Let's see how they work.

Example	If $X \sim B(10, 0.4)$, find:

(a) $P(X \le 3)$ (b) $P(X \le 7)$ (c) $P(X < 5)$

(d) $P(X > 9)$ (e) $P(X \ge 6)$

Solution	Refer to that part of the cumulative table which has $n = 10$ and $p = 0.4$

(a) $P(X \le 3)$ The table gives this as 0.3823

(b) $P(X \le 7)$ The table gives this as 0.9877

(c) $P(X < 5)$ First we re-write this as $P(X \le 4)$. [Remember: X is a *discrete* variable.]

                          The table gives us 0.6331

(d) $P(X > 9)$ First re-write this as $1 - P(X \le 9)$

                          $\therefore$ From the table we get $1 - 0.9999 = 0.0001$

(e) $P(X \ge 6)$ First re-write this as $1 - P(X \le 5)$

                          $\therefore$ From the table we get $1 - 0.8338 = 0.1662$

Example	If $X \sim B(10, 0.6)$ find:
	(a) $P(X \le 4)$ (b) $P(X \ge 7)$

Solution	The trouble here is that the tables only go up as far as $p = 0.5$ and we've got $p = 0.6$! A useful way round this difficulty is as follows:

Given $X \sim B(10, 0.6)$ so let $Y \sim B(10, 0.4)$

(a) $P(X \le 4)$ This is the same as $P(Y \ge 6)$

Now $P(Y \ge 6) = 1 - P(Y \le 5)$

$= 1 - 0.8338 = 0.1662$

(b) $P(X \ge 7)$ This is the same as $P(Y \le 3)$

The tables give this as 0.3823

And so for $X \sim B(n, p)$ with $P > 0.5$ it is useful to introduce

$Y \sim B(n, 1 - p)$ so that:

(a) $P(X \le a)$ is the same as $P(Y \ge n - a)$

and   (b) $P(X \ge b)$ is the same as $P(Y \le n - b)$

Example	If $X \sim B(10, 0.27)$, estimate $P(X \le 6)$.

Solution	This time we've got the problem that $p = 0.27$ and no way can we arrange for that to appear on our table. All we can do, then, is to look at that section of the cumulative table that has $n = 10$ and then look at the columns corresponding to $p = 0.25$ and $p = 0.30$ (because 0.27 is between these two values).

$\therefore$ $P(X \le 6)$ must lie between 0.9965 and 0.9894.

There is no need to attempt linear interpolation. The above should be sufficient for any hypothesis test we carry out.

Practice questions C

For this set of questions you should use your cumulative binomial tables.

1 If $X \sim B(10, 0.2)$, find:
   (a) $P(X \le 3)$ (b) $P(X \ge 6)$.

2 If $X \sim B(20, 0.6)$, find:
   (a) $P(X \le 6)$ (b) $P(X \ge 11)$.

3 If $X \sim B(10, 0.38)$, estimate:
   (a) $P(X \le 3)$ (b) $P(X \ge 6)$.

4 If $X \sim B(20, 0.7)$, find:
   (a) $P(X \le 12)$ (b) $P(X \ge 15)$.

5 Ten years ago 30% of our local woodland trees were silver birch. I think that nowadays there are proportionately more silver birch in our locality. To test this theory I selected 20 trees at random and found that 11 were silver birch. Using your cumulative tables, carry out a hypothesis test at the 2% level of significance. Clearly state H_0, AH and your conclusion.   **C** 3.2

6 Last year 15% of the eggs laid by a flock of chickens were soft-shelled. I think the proportion has changed this year and to test the theory, I sampled 20 eggs and found that 7 were soft-shelled. Using your cumulative tables, carry out a hypothesis test at the 4% level of significance. State H_0, AH and your conclusions clearly.   **C** 3.2

We have seen, then, how to carry out a hypothesis test using a single observation from a binomial distribution. We now have to carry out a similar procedure for the mean of a Poisson distribution.

Testing a theory involving the mean of a Poisson distribution

OCR S2 5.12.4 (i)

Let's look at the procedure with a worked example.

| **Example** | On my walks last year I reckoned to see an average of 2 rabbits per walk. During three walks this year I've seen a *total* of 11 rabbits. Assuming a Poisson distribution, carry out a hypothesis test at the 5% level to determine whether the mean number of rabbits seen on this year's walks has increased. |

| **Solution** | First of all there are *3 walks* $\therefore$ The expected mean = 6. |

That gives us $H_0 : \mu = 6$

As for the alternative hypothesis, the critical words in the question are 'has increased'.

That gives us $AH : \mu > 6$

Since the level of significance is 5% that gives us Fig. 4.6.

Figure 4.6

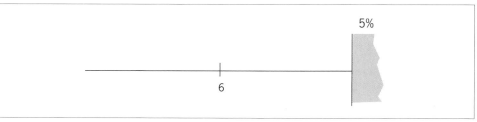

We now have to see whether the observed total of 11 lies in the shaded area.

$$\therefore \quad P(x \geq 11) = P(11, 12, 13, \ldots)$$
$$= 1 - P(x \leq 10)$$
$$= 1 - \left[e^{-6} + \frac{e^{-6}6}{1!} + \frac{e^{-6}6^2}{2!} + \frac{e^{-6}6^3}{3!} + \frac{e^{-6}6^4}{4!} + \frac{e^{-6}6^5}{5!} + \frac{e^{-6}6^6}{6!} \right.$$
$$\left. + \frac{e^{-6}6^7}{7!} + \frac{e^{-6}6^8}{8!} + \frac{e^{-6}6^9}{9!} + \frac{e^{-6}6^{10}}{10!} \right]$$
$$= 1 - e^{-6}\left[1 + \frac{6}{1!} + \frac{6^2}{2!} + \frac{6^3}{3!} + \ldots + \frac{6^{10}}{10!} \right]$$
$$= 0.0426$$

i.e. there is a 4.26% chance of seeing 11 or more. This is inside the shaded tail and so we accept AH.

$\therefore$ The mean number of rabbits seen on this year's walks has increased.

Once again, there are cumulative probability tables for the Poisson distribution (see Appendix 2 on p. 70); they work in the same way as before, and you may be expected to use them in your exam.

Practice questions D

C 3.2

Use your cumulative Poisson tables for these questions.

1 (a) $X \sim P(2.5)$. Find $P(X \le 5)$.
    (b) $X \sim P(4.5)$. Find $P(X \ge 8)$.
    (c) $X \sim P(8)$. Find $P(X \ge 12)$.

2 The number of parking tickets issued by a traffic warden in the local town followed a Poisson distribution with mean 1.8 per day. We've now got two traffic wardens and on the last four days they have issued a total of 12 tickets. Test at the 5% level whether the additional warden has led to an increase in the number of tickets issued. State H_0, AH and your conclusion clearly.

3 An experienced teacher uses an average of 1.2 pieces of chalk per day and this can be assumed to follow a Poisson distribution. When she took sick leave, a supply teacher took over her classes and in five days used a total of 11 pieces of chalk. Test at the 5% level of significance whether there was a change in the mean number of pieces of chalk used.

4 An employee is seeking a typist who can be relied upon to mistype no more than 0.8 characters per page on average. An applicant for the position is given 5 pages to type and, on inspection, it was found that he had mistyped a total of 8 characters. Use a 5% significance level to test the hypothesis that his average number of mistyped characters per page is 0.8 against the alternative hypothesis that it is greater than 0.8. Assume a Poisson distribution.

5 The number of aircraft last year flying overhead per day followed a Poisson distribution with mean 1.3. Over the last 5 days this year I have seen 0, 1, 1, 0, 1 aircraft flying overhead. Is there evidence at the 10% level that the mean number of aircraft flying overhead this year has decreased?

If a Poisson distribution has a mean greater than 10, then we have seen that it is approximately normal (but we must remember to use the continuity correction). Let's look at an example of this type.

Example

A motoring organisation knows that in a particular city area, it will receive an average of 12 calls per hour from its members requiring assistance with a broken-down car. In one particular hour there were 15 call-outs. Does this indicate that the average number of call-outs per hour has increased? Use a 1% level of significance and assume that call-outs follow a Poisson distribution.

Solution

A Poisson distribution with mean 12 (and hence variance 12) is approximately normal. And so, bearing in mind that the question asks about 'an increase', we have

$H_0 : \mu = 12$

$AH : \mu > 12$ giving us

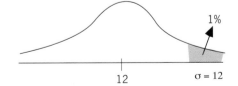

Since our sample reading was 15 we want to find $P(x \ge 15)$ but *allowing for the continuity correction*, this becomes $P(x \ge 14.5)$.

The corresponding Z value (test statistic) is $\dfrac{14.5 - 12}{\sqrt{12}} = 0.72$,

giving us a cumulative total of 0.7642, i.e. $P(x \ge 14.5) = 0.2358$

But 23.58% is well within the acceptance region.

∴ We accept H_0

∴ There is no evidence of an increase in the average number of call-outs per hour.

Practice questions E

1 Manufactured cloth is regarded as being acceptable provided the average number of flaws per metre length is less than 0.5. Inspection of 100 metres revealed a total of 32 flaws. Assuming that the number of flaws per metre has a Poisson distribution, use a 1% significance level to test whether the cloth is acceptable.

2 An established technician repairs on average a computer 1.4 times a week. A new technician is employed and, during his first 15 weeks he repaired a computer 12 times. Use a 5% significance level to test the hypothesis that the average number of repairs has not changed. Assume that the number of times a technician is required to repair a computer has a Poisson distribution.

3 Last year, the number of cups of tea that a senior citizen had during the day followed a Poisson distribution with mean 4.5. On a Monday this year, a random sample of 30 senior citizens drank 150 cups of tea. Is there evidence at the 5% level of significance that this year, senior citizens are drinking more tea on average?

4 With normal grooming, the number of mites on a dog follows a Poisson distribution with mean 3. A 'dog spray' is meant to reduce the average. Checking the new spray out, I sampled 12 dogs and, between them, they had 28 mites. Is there evidence at the 10% level that the new spray reduces the average number of mites per dog?

SUMMARY EXERCISE

1 Over a long period of time it has been found that in Enrico's restaurant the ratio of non-vegetarian to vegetarian meals ordered is 3 to 1.

During one particular day at Enrico's restaurant, a random sample of 20 people contained 2 who ordered a vegetarian meal.

(a) Carry out a significance test to determine whether or not the proportion of vegetarian meals ordered that day is lower than is usual. State clearly your hypotheses and use a 10% significance level.

(b) State an assumption you need to make when carrying out this test. Give one reason why this assumption may well not hold in practice. **C** 3.2

2 State conditions under which the Poisson distribution is a suitable model to use in statistical work.

The number of typing errors per 1000 words made by a typist has a Poisson distribution with mean 2.5.

(a) Find, to 3 d.p., the probability that in an essay of 4000 words there will be at least 12 typing errors.

The typist types 3 essays, each of 4000 words long.

(b) Find the probability that each contains at least 12 typing errors.

A new typist is employed and in a 3000 word essay, 4 typing errors were found.

(c) Perform a significance test at the 5% level to decide whether or not the number of typing errors has decreased. State clearly the hypotheses you use.

3 Records of absenteeism from a factory showed that the number of absentees per day had a Poisson distribution with mean 1.3. During four weeks of 20 working days there were a total of 38 absentees recorded. Use a 2% level of significance to determine whether there is evidence that the average number of absentees has increased.

[AEB]

SUMMARY　　　In this section we have looked at **hypothesis testing** and seen that:

- **1-tail tests** at the **5% level of significance** use:

either

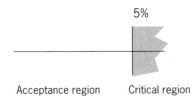

- 5%

Acceptance region　　Critical region

or

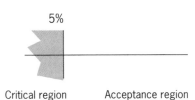

5%

Critical region　　Acceptance region

- **2-tail tests** at the **5% level of significance** use:

$2\frac{1}{2}\%$　　　　　　　　　　　$2\frac{1}{2}\%$

Acceptance region

Critical region　　　　　　Critical region

- We accept the null hypothesis H_0 if the sample reading is in the acceptance region.
- We accept the alternative hypothesis AH if the sample reading is in the critical region.

For testing a **binomial model** we have:

- $H_0 : p = k$
  and then either AH : $p < k$ or AH : $p > k$ or AH : $p \neq k$.

- Cumulative probability tables may have to be used.

For testing a **Poisson model** we have:

- $H_0 : \mu = m$
  and then either AH : $\mu < m$ or AH : $\mu > m$ or AH : $\mu \neq m$.

- Cumulative probability tables may have to be used.
- If $m > 10$ we can use a normal approximation (including the continuity correction).

ANSWERS

Practice questions A

1 (a) $H_0 :$ $p = 0.35$
      AH : $p < 0.35$

    (b) $H_0 :$ $p = 0.15$
      AH : $p > 0.15$

    (c) $H_0 :$ $p = 0.7$
      AH : $p > 0.7$

    (d) $H_0 :$ $p = 0.9$
      AH : $p < 0.9$

    (e) $H_0 :$ $p = 0.75$
      AH : $p \neq 0.75$

2 (a) $H_0 :$ $p = 0.35$
      AH : $p < 0.35$

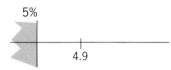

    P $x \leq 2) = 0.0839$, i.e. 8.39%.
This is within the acceptance region.
Accept H_0. I am correct.

    (b) $H_0 :$ $p = 0.15$
      AH : $p > 0.15$

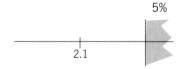

    $P(x \geq 5) = 0.0467$, i.e. 4.67%.
This is in the critical region.
Accept AH. More than 15% are everlasting.

    (c) $H_0 :$ $p = 0.7$
      AH : $p > 0.7$

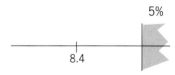

    $P(x \geq 11) = 0.085$, i.e. 8.5%.
This is in the acceptance region.
Accept H_0. The rival firm is no better.

    (d) $H_0 :$ $p = 0.9$
      AH : $p < 0.9$

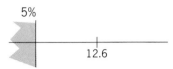

    $P(x \leq 10) = 0.0441$, i.e. 4.41%.
This is in the critical region.
Accept AH. Less than 90% of seeds germinate.

3 $H_0 : p = 0.5$, AH $: p > \frac{1}{2}$
$P(x \geq 7) = 0.035$
Accept AH. There is a bias towards heads.

4 $P(x \geq 9) = 0.073$
Accept H_0. There is no evidence of bias.

5 $P(x \geq 2) = 0.47$
Accept H_0. There is no evidence of an increase.

6 $P(x \geq 6) = 0.042$.
Accept AH. There is evidence that $p > \frac{1}{3}$.

7 $P(x \geq 18) = 0.0355$.
Accept AH. There is evidence of a higher rate of germination.

8 $P(x \leq 2) = 0.151$.
Accept H_0. The 'Shine' claim is justified.

Practice questions B

1 $H_0 : p = 0.5$
    AH $: p \neq 0.5$

    $P(x \geq 6)$ $= 0.144$, i.e. 14.4%.

This is within the acceptance region.
Accept H_0. The coin is fair.
$\therefore$ You are not surprised.

$P(x \geq 7) = 0.035$, i.e. 3.5%.

Still accept H_0. You are still not surprised.

2 $P(x \leq 1)$ $= 0.26$.
Since 26% > $2\frac{1}{2}$%. Accept H_0. The die is OK.

3 Accept H_0 : The coin seems fair.

4 $H_0 : p = 0.2$
  AH $: p \neq 0.2$

  2%   2%

                3.6

  $P(x \geq 8) = 0.0163$, i.e. 1.63%.
  This is inside the critical region
  $\therefore$ Accept AH.
  $\therefore$ Number with faulty brakes has changed.

Practice questions C

1 (a) 0.8791   (b) 0.0064

2 (a) $P(Y \geq 14) = 0.0065$
  (b) $P(Y \leq 9) = 0.7553$

3 (a) Between 0.5138 and 0.3823
  (b) Between 0.0949 and 0.1662

4 (a) 0.2277   (b) 0.4164

5 $H_0 : p = 0.3$
  AH $: p > 0.3$
  $P(x \geq 11) = 1 - 0.9829 = 0.0171$, i.e. 1.71%.
  This is inside the critical region.
  $\therefore$ Accept AH.
  $\therefore$ The proportion has increased.

6 $H_0 : p = 0.15$
  AH $: p \neq 0.15$
  $P(x \geq 7) = 0.0219$, i.e. 2.19%.
  This is greater than 2% (a 2-tail test).
  $\therefore$ Accept H_0. Same proportion as last year.

Practice questions D

1 (a) 0.9580
  (b) $1 - 0.9134 = 0.0866$
  (c) $1 - 0.8881 = 0.1119$

2 $H_0 : \mu = 7.2$
  AH $: \mu > 7.2$
  $P(x \geq 12)$ is between 0.0533 and 0.0792,
  i.e. is between 5.33% and 7.92%.
  Within acceptance region.
  Accept H_0, Mean number of tickets is unchanged.

3 $H_0 : \mu = 6$
  AH $: \mu \neq 6$

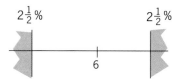

  $2\frac{1}{2}$ % $2\frac{1}{2}$ %

                6

  $P(x \geq 11) = 0.0426$, i.e. 4.26%
  $\therefore$ Within acceptance region.
  $\therefore$ Mean unchanged.

4 $H_0 : \mu = 4$
  AH $: \mu > 4$
  $P(x \geq 8) = 0.0511$, i.e. 5.11%.
  Within acceptance region. Accept H_0.
  He qualifies for the job!

5 $H_0 : \mu = 6.5$
  AH $: \mu < 6.5$
  $P(x \leq 3) = 0.1118$, i.e. 11.18%.
  Within acceptance region. Accept H_0.
  No change in the average number of aircraft
  overhead.

Practice questions E

1 $H_0 : \mu = 50$
  AH $: \mu < 50$
  $P(x \leq 32\frac{1}{2}) = 0.0068$.
  Since 0.68% < 1%. Accept AH.
  The cloth is acceptable.

2 $H_0 : \mu = 21$
  AH $: \mu \neq 21$
  $P(x \leq 12\frac{1}{2}) = 0.032$.
  Since 3.2% $\geq$ 2.5%. Accept H_0.
  The average hasn't changed.

3 $H_0 : \mu = 135$
  AH $: \mu > 135$
  $P(x \geq 149\frac{1}{2}) = 0.1062$.
  Accept H_0. The mean is unchanged.
  $\therefore$ No evidence.

4 $H_0 : \mu = 36$
  AH $: \mu < 36$
  $P(x \leq 28\frac{1}{2}) = 0.1056$.
  Since 10.56% > 10%, H_0 is *just* acceptable.
  Suggest a re-trial with the dog spray.

S2

Practice examination paper

(Attempt all 8 questions.)

1 All packets of cereal produced by 'Healthy Foods' carry a unique identification number that enables the company to trace the packet of cereal through its production process and monitor the staff and machinery involved. The consumer organisation 'What Food?' wishes to test the claim that 'Healthy Foods' cereals contain more nuts than other comparable makers.

'Healthy Foods' have agreed to allow 'What Food?' to take a sample of 20 from their production on January 3rd.

(a) Explain why a sample not a census will have to be taken.

(b) Suggest a suitable sampling frame.

(c) Criticise the company's choice of January 3rd.

 C 3.2

2 An ordinary unbiased die is thrown 900 times. Using a suitable approximation, estimate the probability of obtaining at least 140 sixes.

3 Of the sweets made by a manufacturer, 35% are black. I pick out eight sweets from a packet, with my eyes closed. Assuming that the contents of the packet of sweets is a random sample of the manufacturer's output, find the probability that

(a) exactly three of the eight are black

(b) more than two are black

4 The proportion of faulty televisions sold by a store has been found to be 0.025. During the sales, the store sold 148 televisions. The number of which will be returned as faulty is X. Assuming independence, state the exact distribution of X. Explain why this distribution can be approximated by a Poisson distribution. **C 3.2**

Calculate the probability that no more than 4 televisions will be returned as faulty.

5 A random variable X has probability density function

$$f(x) = \begin{cases} \frac{1}{48}(x-1) & 3 \le x \le 11 \\ 0 & \text{otherwise} \end{cases}$$

(a) Sketch the probability density function of X.

(b) For all values of X, find the cumulative distribution function of X.

(c) Find $P(X \ge 9)$.

(d) Show that the lower quartile of X is given by $1 + 2\sqrt{7}$.

6 A seed producer claims a germination rate of 85% for her carrot seeds. A random sample of 20 seeds was planted, each under under similar conditions, and 14 germinated. Use an exact binomial model to test, at the 10% significance level, the null hypothesis $p = 0.95$ against the alternative hypothesis $p < 0.95$. (You should use cumulative binomial probability tables when answering this question.)

7 The random variable X has a uniform continuous distribution over the interval $-6 \le X \le 3$.

(a) Sketch the probability density function of X.

(b) Show that the largest root of the quadratic equation
$$b^2 - 4b - X = 0$$
is given by $b = 2 + \sqrt{X + 4}$

(c) Show that the probability that this largest root exceeds 3 is $\frac{2}{3}$.

Question 8 follows on next page

8   State conditions under which the Poisson distribution is a suitable model to use in statistical work.

Flaws in a certain brand of tape occur at random and at an average of 0.75 per 100 metres. Assuming a Poisson distribution for the number of flaws, find the probability that in a 400 metre roll of tape,

(a) there will be at least one flaw,

(b) there will be at most 2 flaws.

Find the probability that in a batch of 5 rolls, each of length 400 metres, all rolls will contain fewer than 3 flaws.

A new brand of tape is developed, and in a kilometre of this new tape, 4 flaws were found. Stating your hypotheses and using a 5% significance level decide whether or not this new tape is an improvement on the previous one.

 C 3.2

S2

Solutions

Section 1

1 $X \sim B(10, 0.15)$

$$P(X \geq 4) = 1 - P(X \leq 3)$$
$$= 1 - \left[P(X = 0) + P(X = 1) \right.$$
$$\left. + P(X = 2) + P(X = 3) \right]$$
$$= 1 - \left[(0.85)^{10} + 10\,(0.85)^9\,(0.15) \right.$$
$$+ 45\,(0.85)^8\,(0.15)^2$$
$$\left. + 120\,(0.85)^7\,(0.15)^3 \right]$$
$$= 0.05$$

$E(X) = 10 \times 0.15 = 1.5$

$$P(X > 1.5) = P(X \geq 2) = 1 - P(X \leq 1)$$
$$= 1 - (0.85)^{10} - 10(0.85)^9\,(0.15) \quad = 0.46$$

2   (a) $X \sim B(5, 0.35)$

$P(X = 0) \quad = (0.65)^5 = 0.1160$

$P(X = 1) \quad = 5 \times 0.35 \times 0.65^4 = 0.3124$

$P(X = 2) \quad = {}^5C_2 \times 0.35^2 \times 0.65^3 = 0.3364$

$P(X = 3) \quad = {}^5C_3 \times 0.35^3 \times 0.65^2 = 0.1811$

$P(X = 4) \quad = 5 \times 0.35^4 \times 0.65 = 0.0488$

$P(X = 5) \quad = 0.35^5 = 0.0053$

$E(X) \quad = 5 \times 0.35 = 1.75$

$Var(X) \quad = 1.75 \times 0.65 = 1.1375$

(b)   We need $np = 1$,

i.e. $5p = 1$, so that $p = 0.2$

Then $P(X > 1) = 1 - P(X = 0) - P(X = 1)$
$$= 1 - 0.8^5 - 5 \times 0.8^4 \times 0.2 = 0.26272$$

3   Let n = number of throws required. Then the distribution of X the number of hits is
$X \sim B(n, 0.4)$

For this distribution we require

$\quad\quad P(X \geq 1) \geq 0.9$

$\Rightarrow \quad P(X < 1) \leq 0.1$

$\Rightarrow \quad P(X = 0) \leq 0.1$

$\Rightarrow \quad (0.6)^n \leq 0.1$

$\Rightarrow \quad n \log(0.6) \leq \log(0.1)$

$\Rightarrow \quad n \geq \dfrac{\log 0.1}{\log 0.6} = 4.508$

$\Rightarrow \quad n = 5$

4   (a) $(0.8)^{10} + \binom{10}{1}(0.8)^9(0.2) + \binom{10}{2}(0.8)^8\,(0.2)^2$
$$+ \binom{10}{3}(0.8)^7\,(0.2)^3$$
$$= 0.8791$$

(b) $\binom{10}{7}(0.2)^7\,(0.8)^3 + \binom{10}{8}(0.2)^8\,(0.8)^2$
$$+ \binom{10}{9}(0.2)^9\,(0.8) + (0.2)^{10} = 0.0009$$

(c) $\binom{10}{4}(0.2)^4\,(0.8)^6 + \binom{10}{5}(0.2)^5$
$$+ \binom{10}{6}(0.2)^6\,(0.8)^4 + \binom{10}{7}(0.2)^7\,(0.8)^3$$
$$= 0.1208$$

5 $(0.2)^{10} + \binom{10}{1}(0.2)^9\,(0.8) + \binom{10}{2}(0.2)^8\,(0.8)^2 +$
$\binom{10}{3}(0.2)^7\,(0.8)^3 = 0.0009$

6   Let X = number sold per week

then $X \sim P(4)$

(a) $P(X \geq 2) = 1 - P(X = 0) - P(X = 1)$
$$= 1 - e^{-4} - 4e^{-4}$$
$$= 0.91$$

(b)   Keep adding up

$P(X = 0) + P(X = 1) \quad + \ldots$

until 0.99 at least is obtained.

So need to make

$$e^{-4}\left[1 + 4 + \frac{4^2}{2!} + \frac{4^3}{3!} + \frac{4^4}{4!} + \ldots \right] \geq .99$$

i.e. need

$$\left[1 + 4 + \frac{4^2}{2!} + \frac{4^3}{3!} + \frac{4^4}{4!} + \ldots \right] \geq 54.0522$$

By trial and error 9 radios should be held.

(c)   Sales are random in time although may be affected by advertising campaigns and seasonal factors.

7 X = number of accidents per week

$X \sim P(2.5)$

(a) $P(X = 5) = \dfrac{2.5^5\,e^{-2.5}}{5!} = 0.067$

(b)   If Y is the number of accidents in 2 weeks, then $Y \sim P(5)$

$\therefore$ P$(Y > 5)$ $= 1 - $ P (0 or 1 or 2 or 3 or 4 or 5 accidents)

$= 1 - e^{-5}\left(1 + \frac{5}{1!} + \frac{5^2}{2!} + \frac{5^3}{3!} + \frac{5^4}{4!} + \frac{5^5}{5!}\right)$

$= 0.384$

8 $X \sim$ B(35, 0.1)

$\Rightarrow X \approx$ P(3.5)

P$(X \le 5) \approx e^{-3.5}\Big[1 + 3.5 + \frac{3.5^2}{2!} + \frac{3.5^3}{3!}$
$+ \frac{3.5^4}{4!} + \frac{3.5^5}{5!}\Big]$

≈ 0.858

Section 2

1   (a) $\displaystyle\int_0^{0.6} 10\,cx^2\,dx + \int_{0.6}^1 9c\,(1 - x)\,dx = 1$

$\Rightarrow \left[\dfrac{10cx^3}{3}\right]_0^{0.6} + \left[9cx - \dfrac{9cx^2}{2}\right]_{0.6}^1 = 1$

$\Rightarrow \quad 0.72c + 9c - 4.5c - 5.4c + 1.62c = 1$

$\Rightarrow \quad 1.44c = 1 \Rightarrow c = \dfrac{25}{36}$

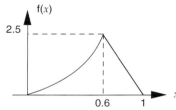

(b)   Mode $= 0.6$

(c)   P$(X < 0.4) = \displaystyle\int_0^{0.4} 10cx^2\,dx$

$= \left[\dfrac{10c\,x^3}{3}\right]_0^{0.4}$

$= \dfrac{10}{3} \times \dfrac{25}{36} \times 0.4^3 \qquad = 0.15$

2 $\displaystyle\int_0^1 6kx\,(1 - x)\,dx + \int_1^\infty \frac{k}{x^2}\,dx = 1$

$\Rightarrow 6k\displaystyle\int_0^1 (x - x^2)\,dx + k\int_1^\infty x^{-2}\,dx = 1$

$\Rightarrow 6k\left[\dfrac{x^2}{2} - \dfrac{x^3}{3}\right]_0^1 + k\left[\dfrac{-1}{x}\right]_1^\infty = 1$

$\Rightarrow 6k\left(\dfrac{1}{2} - \dfrac{1}{3}\right) + k\,(0 + 1) = 1$

$\Rightarrow k + k = 1 \Rightarrow k = \dfrac{1}{2}$

P$\left(X > \dfrac{1}{2}\right) = \displaystyle\int_{1/2}^1 6kx\,(1 - x)\,dx + \int_1^\infty \frac{k}{x^2}\,dx$

or more simply using the complement

$\begin{aligned}
\text{P}\left(X > \tfrac{1}{2}\right) &= 1 - \text{P}\left(X \le \tfrac{1}{2}\right)\\[4pt]
&= 1 - \int_0^{1/2} 6kx(1 - x)\,dx\\[4pt]
&= 1 - \int_0^{1/2} (3x - 3x^2)\,dx\\[4pt]
&= 1 - \left[\frac{3x^2}{2} - x^3\right]_0^{1/2} = \frac{3}{4}
\end{aligned}$

3 $F(x) = \displaystyle\int_0^x 3t(1-t)\,dt$

$\quad = \left[\dfrac{3t^2}{2} - t^3 \right]_0^x$

$\quad = \dfrac{3x^2}{2} - x^3 \text{ for } 0 < x < 1$

$F(x) = F(1) + \displaystyle\int_1^x \dfrac{1}{2t^2}\,dt$

$\quad = \dfrac{1}{2} + \left[\dfrac{-1}{2t} \right]_1^x$

$\quad = \dfrac{1}{2} + \left[\dfrac{-1}{2x} + \dfrac{1}{2} \right]$

$\quad = 1 - \dfrac{1}{2x} \text{ for } x \geq 1$

Hence

$F(x) = \begin{cases} 0 & x \leq 0 \\ \dfrac{3x^2}{2} - x^3 & 0 < x \leq 1 \\ 1 - \dfrac{1}{2x} & x \geq 1 \end{cases}$

(a) $F\left(\dfrac{1}{2}\right) = \dfrac{3}{2}\left(\dfrac{1}{2}\right)^2 - \left(\dfrac{1}{2}\right)^3$

$\quad = \dfrac{3}{8} - \dfrac{1}{8} = \dfrac{1}{4}$

(b) $F(5) = 1 - \dfrac{1}{10} = \dfrac{9}{10}$

$\quad$ so $P(X \leq 5) = \dfrac{9}{10}$

4 (a) $f(x) = \dfrac{d}{dx} F(x)$

$\quad = \dfrac{d}{dx}\left[\dfrac{6}{1000}\left(5x^2 - \dfrac{1}{3}x^3\right) \right]$

$\quad = \dfrac{6}{1000}(10x - x^2)$

In full PDF is

$f(x) = \begin{cases} 0 & x \leq 0 \\ \dfrac{6}{1000}(10x - x^2) & 0 \leq x \leq 10 \\ 0 & x > 10 \end{cases}$

The PDF of X:

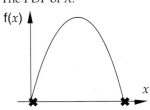

(b) P(Tube does not fail in first two years)

$\quad = P(X > 2) = 1 - P(X \leq 2) = 1 - F(2)$

$\quad = 1 - \dfrac{6}{1000}\left(20 - \dfrac{8}{3}\right) = \dfrac{112}{125}$

For 8 tubes probability $= \left(\dfrac{112}{125}\right)^8 \sim 0.42$

(c) Let B = event 'tube lasts at least two years'.
Then $P(B) = \dfrac{112}{125}$

and let A = event 'tube lasts at least four years'

then we require $P(A \mid B) = \dfrac{P(A \cap B)}{P(B)}$

$A \cap B$ is tube lasts two years and tube last four years which reduces to tube lasts four years.

$P(X > 4) = 1 - P(X \leq 4) = 1 - F(4) = \dfrac{648}{1000}$

Hence $P(A \mid B) = \dfrac{\frac{648}{1000}}{\frac{896}{1000}} = \dfrac{648}{896} = \dfrac{81}{112}$

(d) No tube can last more than 10 years with this model. Unlikely to be a symmetrical distribution – more likely to have a positive skew.

5 (a) $\displaystyle\int_0^2 kx(2-x)\,dx = 1$

$\quad \Rightarrow k\left[x^2 - \dfrac{x^3}{3} \right]_0^2 = 1$

$\quad \Rightarrow k\dfrac{4}{3} = 1 \Rightarrow k = \dfrac{3}{4}$

(b) Mode = 1

(c) Median = 1

both by symmetry (or calculus)

6 (a) $f(x) = \dfrac{dF(x)}{dx}$

$\quad \therefore f(x) = \begin{cases} 5x^4 & 0 \leq x \leq 1 \\ 0 & \text{otherwise} \end{cases}$

(b) $\left[x^5 \right]_0^{0.2} = 0.00032$

(c) $n^5 = \dfrac{1}{32} \quad \therefore n = \dfrac{1}{2}$

Section 3

1 $E(X) = \dfrac{3 + (-1)}{2} = 1$

$\text{Var}(X) = \dfrac{(3 - (-1))^2}{12} = \dfrac{4}{3}$

$P(X > 0) = \dfrac{3}{4}$

$F(x) = \dfrac{x - (-1)}{3 - (-1)} = \dfrac{x + 1}{4}$

In full

$F(x) = \begin{cases} 0 & x < -1 \\ \dfrac{x + 1}{4} & 1 \le x \le 3 \\ 1 & x > 3 \end{cases}$

PDF of X

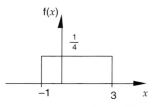

CDF of X

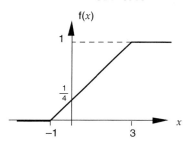

2 $X \sim B(200, 0.45)$

$\Rightarrow X \approx N(90, 49.5)$

(a) $P(X \le 76) \approx P(X \le 76.5)$
      (using continuity correction)

Let $Z = \dfrac{X - 90}{7.04}$

then $P(X \le 76.5) = P(Z \le -1.92)$

$= 1 - P(Z \le 1.92)$

$= 1 - 0.973 = 0.03 \ (2 \text{ d.p.})$

(b) $P(X > 110) = 1 - P(X \le 110)$

$\approx 1 - P(X \le 110.5)$
      (continuity correction)

$P(X \le 110.5) \approx P(Z \le 2.91) = 0.998$

so $P(X > 110) = 0.002$

(c) $P(80 \le X < 100)$

$= P(X \le 99) - P(X \le 79)$

$\approx P(X \le 99.5) - P(X \le 79.5)$
      (by continuity correction)

$= P(Z \le 1.349) - P(Z \le -1.492)$

$= P(Z \le 1.349) - (1 - P(Z \le 1.492))$

$= 0.912 - (1 - 0.932) = 0.844$

3   (a) $P(\text{more than } 3) = P(4 \text{ or } 5 \text{ or } 6 \text{ or } 7)$

$= \dfrac{7!}{4!3!}(0.4)^4(0.6)^3 + \dfrac{7!}{5!2!}(0.4)^5(0.6)^2$

$\qquad + \dfrac{7!}{6!1!}(0.4)^6(0.6) + (0.4)^7$

$= 0.290$

(b) $n = 700, \ p = 0.4$

$\therefore \text{Mean} = np = 700 \times 0.4 = 280$

And Variance $= np(1 - p)$

$= 700 \times 0.4 \times 0.6 = 168 \quad \therefore \sigma = \sqrt{168}$

More than 300 means we need the shaded area in the following diagram:

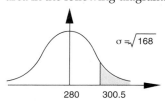

Now $Z = \dfrac{300.5 - 280}{\sqrt{168}} = 1.582$

The standard normal tables give 0.9431

$\therefore \text{Ans} = 0.0569$

4 $14 > 10 \quad \therefore X \approx N(14, 14)$

$\therefore \quad Z = \dfrac{16\frac{1}{2} - 14}{\sqrt{14}}$ giving a final answer of 0.252

5 $\dfrac{n - \frac{1}{2} - 20}{\sqrt{20}} = 1.23 \ \Rightarrow n = 26$

Section 4

1 (a) $H_0 : p = \frac{1}{4}$

AH : $p < \frac{1}{4}$ ∴

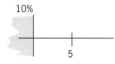

10%

5

$P(x \leq 2) = 0.0913$, i.e. 9.13%

∴ In critical region. Accept AH.

∴ $p < \frac{1}{4}$

∴ Proportion lower than usual.

(b) Assume it was a 'typical day' – not Christmas Day for example. In practice the day chosen may not be typical.

2 Rare events which occur randomly and independently.

(a) $X \sim P(10)$
$P(X \geq 12)$ $= 0.303$

(b) $(0.303)^3$ $= 0.028$

(c) $H_0 : \mu = 7.5$
AH : $\mu < 7.5$
$P(x \leq 4) = 0.1321$, i.e. 13.21%

In acceptance region. Accept H_0.

New typist has same average number of errors as before.

3 $H_0 : \mu = 26$
AH : $\mu > 26$

Using a normal approximation N(26, 26),
$P(x \geq 37\frac{1}{2}) = 0.012$, i.e. 1.2%

In critical region. Accept AH
Average number of absentees has increased.

Appendix 1: Binomial cumulative distribution function

The tabulated value is $P(X \leq x)$, where X has a binomial distribution with index n and parameter p.

$p =$	0.05	0.10	0.15	0.20	0.25	0.30	0.35	0.40	0.45	0.50
$n = 5, x = 0$	0.7738	0.5905	0.4437	0.3277	0.2373	0.1681	0.1160	0.0778	0.0503	0.0312
1	0.9774	0.9185	0.8352	0.7373	0.6328	0.5282	0.4284	0.3370	0.2562	0.1875
2	0.9988	0.9914	0.9734	0.9421	0.8965	0.8369	0.7648	0.6826	0.5931	0.5000
3	1.0000	0.9995	0.9978	0.9933	0.9844	0.9692	0.9460	0.9130	0.8688	0.8125
4	1.0000	1.0000	0.9999	0.9997	0.9990	0.9976	0.9947	0.9898	0.9815	0.9688
$n = 10, x = 0$	0.5987	0.3487	0.1969	0.1074	0.0563	0.0282	0.0135	0.0060	0.0025	0.0010
1	0.9139	0.7361	0.5443	0.3758	0.2440	0.1493	0.0860	0.0464	0.0233	0.0107
2	0.9885	0.9298	0.8202	0.6778	0.5256	0.3828	0.2616	0.1673	0.0996	0.0547
3	0.9990	0.9872	0.9500	0.8791	0.7759	0.6496	0.5138	0.3823	0.2660	0.1719
4	0.9999	0.9984	0.9901	0.9672	0.9219	0.8497	0.7515	0.6331	0.5044	0.3770
5	1.0000	0.9999	0.9986	0.9936	0.9803	0.9527	0.9051	0.8338	0.7384	0.6230
6	1.0000	1.0000	0.9999	0.9991	0.9965	0.9894	0.9740	0.9452	0.8980	0.8281
7	1.0000	1.0000	1.0000	0.9999	0.9996	0.9984	0.9952	0.9877	0.9726	0.9453
8	1.0000	1.0000	1.0000	1.0000	1.0000	0.9999	0.9995	0.9983	0.9955	0.9893
9	1.0000	1.0000	1.0000	1.0000	1.0000	1.0000	1.0000	0.9999	0.9997	0.9990
$n = 20, x = 0$	0.3585	0.1216	0.0388	0.0115	0.0032	0.0008	0.0002	0.0000	0.0000	0.0000
1	0.7358	0.3917	0.1756	0.0692	0.0243	0.0076	0.0021	0.0005	0.0001	0.0000
2	0.9245	0.6769	0.4049	0.2061	0.0913	0.0355	0.0121	0.0036	0.0009	0.0002
3	0.9841	0.8670	0.6477	0.4114	0.2252	0.1071	0.0444	0.0160	0.0049	0.0013
4	0.9974	0.9568	0.8298	0.6296	0.4148	0.2375	0.1182	0.0510	0.0189	0.0059
5	0.9997	0.9887	0.9327	0.8042	0.6172	0.4164	0.2454	0.1256	0.0553	0.0207
6	1.0000	0.9976	0.9781	0.9133	0.7858	0.6080	0.4166	0.2500	0.1299	0.0577
7	1.0000	0.9996	0.9941	0.9679	0.8982	0.7723	0.6010	0.4159	0.2520	0.1316
8	1.0000	0.9999	0.9987	0.9900	0.9591	0.8867	0.7624	0.5956	0.4143	0.2517
9	1.0000	1.0000	0.9998	0.9974	0.9861	0.9520	0.8782	0.7553	0.5914	0.4119
10	1.0000	1.0000	1.0000	0.9994	0.9961	0.9829	0.9468	0.8725	0.7507	0.5881
11	1.0000	1.0000	1.0000	0.9999	0.9991	0.9949	0.9804	0.9435	0.8692	0.7483
12	1.0000	1.0000	1.0000	1.0000	0.9998	0.9987	0.9940	0.9790	0.9420	0.8684
13	1.0000	1.0000	1.0000	1.0000	1.0000	0.9997	0.9985	0.9935	0.9786	0.9423
14	1.0000	1.0000	1.0000	1.0000	1.0000	1.0000	0.9997	0.9984	0.9936	0.9793
15	1.0000	1.0000	1.0000	1.0000	1.0000	1.0000	1.0000	0.9997	0.9985	0.9941
16	1.0000	1.0000	1.0000	1.0000	1.0000	1.0000	1.0000	1.0000	0.9997	0.9987
17	1.0000	1.0000	1.0000	1.0000	1.0000	1.0000	1.0000	1.0000	1.0000	0.9998
18	1.0000	1.0000	1.0000	1.0000	1.0000	1.0000	1.0000	1.0000	1.0000	1.0000

Appendix 2: Poisson cumulative distribution function

The tabulated value is $P(X \le x)$, where X has a Poisson distribution with parameter μ.

$\mu =$	0.5	1.0	1.5	2.0	2.5	3.0	3.5	4.0	4.5	5.0
$x = 0$	0.6065	0.3679	0.2231	0.1353	0.0821	0.0498	0.0302	0.0183	0.0111	0.0067
1	0.9098	0.7358	0.5578	0.4060	0.2873	0.1991	0.1359	0.0916	0.0611	0.0404
2	0.9856	0.9197	0.8088	0.6767	0.5438	0.4232	0.3208	0.2381	0.1736	0.1247
3	0.9982	0.9810	0.9344	0.8571	0.7576	0.6472	0.5366	0.4335	0.3423	0.2650
4	0.9998	0.9963	0.9814	0.9473	0.8912	0.8153	0.7254	0.6288	0.5321	0.4405
5	1.0000	0.9994	0.9955	0.9834	0.9580	0.9161	0.8576	0.7851	0.7029	0.6160
6	1.0000	0.9999	0.9991	0.9955	0.9858	0.9665	0.9347	0.8893	0.8311	0.7622
7	1.0000	1.0000	0.9998	0.9989	0.9958	0.9881	0.9733	0.9489	0.9134	0.8666
8	1.0000	1.0000	1.0000	0.9998	0.9989	0.9962	0.9901	0.9786	0.9597	0.9319
9	1.0000	1.0000	1.0000	1.0000	0.9997	0.9989	0.9967	0.9919	0.9829	0.9682
10	1.0000	1.0000	1.0000	1.0000	0.9999	0.9997	0.9990	0.9972	0.9933	0.9863
11	1.0000	1.0000	1.0000	1.0000	1.0000	0.9999	0.9997	0.9991	0.9976	0.9945
12	1.0000	1.0000	1.0000	1.0000	1.0000	1.0000	0.9999	0.9997	0.9992	0.9980
13	1.0000	1.0000	1.0000	1.0000	1.0000	1.0000	1.0000	0.9999	0.9997	0.9993
14	1.0000	1.0000	1.0000	1.0000	1.0000	1.0000	1.0000	1.0000	0.9999	0.9998
15	1.0000	1.0000	1.0000	1.0000	1.0000	1.0000	1.0000	1.0000	1.0000	0.9999
16	1.0000	1.0000	1.0000	1.0000	1.0000	1.0000	1.0000	1.0000	1.0000	1.0000
17	1.0000	1.0000	1.0000	1.0000	1.0000	1.0000	1.0000	1.0000	1.0000	1.0000
18	1.0000	1.0000	1.0000	1.0000	1.0000	1.0000	1.0000	1.0000	1.0000	1.0000
19	1.0000	1.0000	1.0000	1.0000	1.0000	1.0000	1.0000	1.0000	1.0000	1.0000
$\mu =$	5.5	6.0	6.5	7.0	7.5	8.0	8.5	9.0	9.5	10.0
$x = 0$	0.0041	0.0025	0.0015	0.0009	0.0006	0.0003	0.0002	0.0001	0.0001	0.0000
1	0.0266	0.0174	0.0113	0.0073	0.0047	0.0030	0.0019	0.0012	0.0008	0.0005
2	0.0884	0.0620	0.0430	0.0296	0.0203	0.0138	0.0093	0.0062	0.0042	0.0028
3	0.2017	0.1512	0.1118	0.0818	0.0591	0.0424	0.0301	0.0212	0.0149	0.0103
4	0.3575	0.2851	0.2237	0.1730	0.1321	0.0996	0.0744	0.0550	0.0403	0.0293
5	0.5289	0.4457	0.3690	0.3007	0.2414	0.1912	0.1496	0.1157	0.0885	0.0671
6	0.6860	0.6063	0.5265	0.4497	0.3782	0.3134	0.2562	0.2068	0.1649	0.1301
7	0.8095	0.7440	0.6728	0.5987	0.5246	0.4530	0.3856	0.3239	0.2687	0.2202
8	0.8944	0.8472	0.7916	0.7291	0.6620	0.5925	0.5231	0.4557	0.3918	0.3328
9	0.9462	0.9161	0.8774	0.8305	0.7764	0.7166	0.6530	0.5874	0.5218	0.4579
10	0.9747	0.9574	0.9332	0.9015	0.8622	0.8159	0.7634	0.7060	0.6453	0.5830
11	0.9890	0.9799	0.9661	0.9467	0.9208	0.8881	0.8487	0.8030	0.7520	0.6968
12	0.9955	0.9912	0.9840	0.9730	0.9573	0.9362	0.9091	0.8758	0.8364	0.7916
13	0.9983	0.9964	0.9929	0.9872	0.9784	0.9658	0.9486	0.9261	0.8981	0.8645
14	0.9994	0.9986	0.9970	0.9943	0.9897	0.9827	0.9726	0.9585	0.9400	0.9165
15	0.9998	0.9995	0.9988	0.9976	0.9954	0.9918	0.9862	0.9780	0.9665	0.9513
16	0.9999	0.9998	0.9996	0.9990	0.9980	0.9963	0.9934	0.9889	0.9823	0.9730
17	1.0000	0.9999	0.9998	0.9996	0.9992	0.9984	0.9970	0.9947	0.9911	0.9857
18	1.0000	1.0000	0.9999	0.9999	0.9997	0.9993	0.9987	0.9976	0.9957	0.9928
19	1.0000	1.0000	1.0000	1.0000	0.9999	0.9997	0.9995	0.9989	0.9980	0.9965
20	1.0000	1.0000	1.0000	1.0000	1.0000	0.9999	0.9998	0.9996	0.9991	0.9984
21	1.0000	1.0000	1.0000	1.0000	1.0000	1.0000	0.9999	0.9998	0.9996	0.9993
22	1.0000	1.0000	1.0000	1.0000	1.0000	1.0000	1.0000	0.9999	0.9999	0.9997

Appendix 3: The normal distribution function

The function tabulated below is $\Phi(z)$, defined as $\Phi(z) = \dfrac{1}{\sqrt{2\pi}} \displaystyle\int_{-\infty}^{z} e^{-\frac{1}{2}t^2}\, \mathrm{d}t.$

z	$\Phi(z)$	z	$\Phi(z)$	z	$\Phi(z)$	z	$\Phi(z)$	z	$\Phi(z)$
0.00	0.5000	0.50	0.6915	1.00	0.8413	1.50	0.9332	2.00	0.9772
0.01	0.5040	0.51	0.6950	1.01	0.8438	1.51	0.9345	2.02	0.9783
0.02	0.5080	0.52	0.6985	1.02	0.8461	1.52	0.9357	2.04	0.9793
0.03	0.5120	0.53	0.7019	1.03	0.8485	1.53	0.9370	2.06	0.9803
0.04	0.5160	0.54	0.7054	1.04	0.8508	1.54	0.9382	2.08	0.9812
0.05	0.5199	0.55	0.7088	1.05	0.8531	1.55	0.9394	2.10	0.9821
0.06	0.5239	0.56	0.7123	1.06	0.8554	1.56	0.9406	2.12	0.9830
0.07	0.5279	0.57	0.7157	1.07	0.8577	1.57	0.9418	2.14	0.9838
0.08	0.5319	0.58	0.7190	1.08	0.8599	1.58	0.9429	2.16	0.9846
0.09	0.5359	0.59	0.7224	1.09	0.8621	1.59	0.9441	2.18	0.9854
0.10	0.5398	0.60	0.7257	1.10	0.8643	1.60	0.9452	2.20	0.9861
0.11	0.5438	0.61	0.7291	1.11	0.8665	1.61	0.9463	2.22	0.9868
0.12	0.5478	0.62	0.7324	1.12	0.8686	1.62	0.9474	2.24	0.9875
0.13	0.5517	0.63	0.7357	1.13	0.8708	1.63	0.9484	2.26	0.9881
0.14	0.5557	0.64	0.7389	1.14	0.8729	1.64	0.9495	2.28	0.9887
0.15	0.5596	0.65	0.7422	1.15	0.8749	1.65	0.9505	2.30	0.9893
0.16	0.5636	0.66	0.7454	1.16	0.8770	1.66	0.9515	2.32	0.9898
0.17	0.5675	0.67	0.7486	1.17	0.8790	1.67	0.9525	2.34	0.9904
0.18	0.5714	0.68	0.7517	1.18	0.8810	1.68	0.9535	2.36	0.9909
0.19	0.5753	0.69	0.7549	1.19	0.8830	1.69	0.9545	2.38	0.9913
0.20	0.5793	0.70	0.7580	1.20	0.8849	1.70	0.9554	2.40	0.9918
0.21	0.5832	0.71	0.7611	1.21	0.8869	1.71	0.9564	2.42	0.9922
0.22	0.5871	0.72	0.7642	1.22	0.8888	1.72	0.9573	2.44	0.9927
0.23	0.5910	0.73	0.7673	1.23	0.8907	1.73	0.9582	2.46	0.9931
0.24	0.5948	0.74	0.7704	1.24	0.8925	1.74	0.9591	2.48	0.9934
0.25	0.5987	0.75	0.7734	1.25	0.8944	1.75	0.9599	2.50	0.9938
0.26	0.6026	0.76	0.7764	1.26	0.8962	1.76	0.9608	2.55	0.9946
0.27	0.6064	0.77	0.7794	1.27	0.8980	1.77	0.9616	2.60	0.9953
0.28	0.6103	0.78	0.7823	1.28	0.8997	1.78	0.9625	2.65	0.9960
0.29	0.6141	0.79	0.7852	1.29	0.9015	1.79	0.9633	2.70	0.9965
0.30	0.6179	0.80	0.7881	1.30	0.9032	1.80	0.9641	2.75	0.9970
0.31	0.6217	0.81	0.7910	1.31	0.9049	1.81	0.9649	2.80	0.9974
0.32	0.6255	0.82	0.7939	1.32	0.9066	1.82	0.9656	2.85	0.9978
0.33	0.6293	0.83	0.7967	1.33	0.9082	1.83	0.9664	2.90	0.9981
0.34	0.6331	0.84	0.7995	1.34	0.9099	1.84	0.9671	2.95	0.9984
0.35	0.6368	0.85	0.8023	1.35	0.9115	1.85	0.9678	3.00	0.9987
0.36	0.6406	0.86	0.8051	1.36	0.9131	1.86	0.9686	3.05	0.9989
0.37	0.6443	0.87	0.8078	1.37	0.9147	1.87	0.9693	3.10	0.9990
0.38	0.6480	0.88	0.8106	1.38	0.9162	1.88	0.9699	3.15	0.9992
0.39	0.6517	0.89	0.8133	1.39	0.9177	1.89	0.9706	3.20	0.9993
0.40	0.6554	0.90	0.8159	1.40	0.9192	1.90	0.9713	3.25	0.9994
0.41	0.6591	0.91	0.8186	1.41	0.9207	1.91	0.9719	3.30	0.9995
0.42	0.6628	0.92	0.8212	1.42	0.9222	1.92	0.9726	3.35	0.9996
0.43	0.6664	0.93	0.8238	1.43	0.9236	1.93	0.9732	3.40	0.9997
0.44	0.6700	0.94	0.8264	1.44	0.9251	1.94	0.9738	3.50	0.9998
0.45	0.6736	0.95	0.8289	1.45	0.9265	1.95	0.9744	3.60	0.9998
0.46	0.6772	0.96	0.8315	1.46	0.9279	1.96	0.9750	3.70	0.9999
0.47	0.6808	0.97	0.8340	1.47	0.9292	1.97	0.9756	3.80	0.9999
0.48	0.6844	0.98	0.8365	1.48	0.9306	1.98	0.9761	3.90	1.0000
0.49	0.6879	0.99	0.8389	1.49	0.9319	1.99	0.9767	4.00	1.0000
0.50	0.6915	1.00	0.8413	1.50	0.9332	2.00	0.9772		

Appendix 4: Key Skills

Your work on this book will provide opportunities for gathering evidence towards Key Skills, especially in Communication and Application of Number.

These opportunities are indicated by the 'key' icon, e.g.   **C** 3.2. This means that the exercise contains the type of task that is relevant to Communication Level 3 and may help you gather evidence specifically for C3.2.

The places where Key Skills references are given are listed below, together with some other ideas about possible opportunities for gathering evidence.

Communication

C3.2   Read and synthesise information from two extended documents that deal with a complex subject. One of these documents should include at least one image.

See pages 4, 5, 6, 10, 11, 13, 30, 42, 44, 50, 52, 53, 55, 56, 61 and 62 of this book.

Your work on S2 provides lots of opportunities for reading and synthesising information, especially if you carry out any project that involves analysing tables or statistical diagrams.